SCHEMES

a novella

Peagerm Press

ISBN 978-1-3999-8268-9

contact us at:

peagermpress@gmail.com

Back cover photo
by Rut Harwood

SCHEMES

keep ya busy, make ya dizzy

1

So there I was, on a train, heading south towards The Smoke. Not my final destination, but a decent stop-off point. I was chasing down a job and off to tackle my very first interview. Having only just left school it all felt like a big adventure.

Beechers was the company name and pharmaceuticals was the game, they ran it from a complex in a sleepy town along the coast. They'd booked me into a posh hotel along with all the other participants. Everything was paid for and it seemed that life had just begun.

I found the place and settled in. A meal was booked for 7 p.m. A company rep was going to meet us and guide us through the interview process. That was good, they really cared. I ran myself a nice, hot bath. Next I knew I was sat in the restaurant, slurping down a glass of wine. The rep seemed like a pleasant chap, balding with a neat moustache. What surprised me though was that there seemed to be only two other candidates. Right away I asked the question: "How many jobs are available here?" Up to three, apparently, as long as everyone met the standard. Ouch, that was a wake up call, they'd picked me for my chemistry skills. Unfortunately there was a snag: it looked as though I'd failed the exam. No, I was *sure* I'd failed, we hadn't had our results as yet, but one of the papers had been a disaster and we were required to pass all three. Oh well, maybe I could resit, it would take another year but this job would have gone by then so I necked the wine and had a refill.

I awoke, hungover of course, but free drinks were a rarity and not being that gregarious I needed a few to get me going. The others had seemed much more relaxed, a Yorkshire lad and a lass from Leigh; I'd seen the former on the train, the latter only in my dreams. The guy was not as tall as me but carried himself with much more dignity, he had also grown a moustache, quite mature for just eighteen. The girl meanwhile looked stunning with her long brown hair and big green eyes and naturally they'd hit it off while I just sat there getting drunk.

I saw them in the dining room, tucking into a hearty breakfast. I just sat there suffering with a slice of toast and a jug of orange juice.

"Why not join us?" 'tache-man said.

"Thanks, but no, I might throw up on ya!"

He just laughed and muttered something. Some folks had it all worked out.

The three of us arrived at Beechers, out towards the edge of town, where we were led to a comfortable lounge before setting off on a company tour. The interviews were staggered while the other two were left to stew, but what was really staggering was the assessor was the company rep! Oh, that was sneaky, he'd been masquerading as hospitality, yet, here he was in charge having already seen us with our guards down! My guard had been so far down you could almost see the soles of my feet, I seemed to remember slavvering on about how punk rock could save the world. Well, it didn't matter much, I knew I wasn't getting the job, so I just smiled and ploughed ahead and put the whole thing down to experience.

2

Then my A-level grades were in: a 'D' an 'E' and a miserable 'O'. Another year of schooling? No, I signed up for a BTEC instead. Computer Studies. Well, why not? Computers were the future and a BTEC gave you work experience, I could get a step ahead. The classes were in Darleston, an hour or so away on the bus, the college just a gentle walk, and there I was, once again, back to being a full-time student. There were twelve of us on the course, a motley crew but all quite friendly, mostly male but bright it seemed and always quick to add some humour.

Coursework was a doddle, all those bits and bytes made perfect sense, I had a scientific brain and logic came as second nature. Lunchtimes did seem awkward though, my classmates all went down the pub and though I would have loved to join them I had sandwiches instead. Though the course was funded I had travelling costs to deal with and although I didn't pay much board I always needed lots of records. I was relatively shy and alcohol did help that way but life meant making choices and I made the choice to eat alone.

The BTEC had a special purpose, it was now the PC age and every business needed them and folks like us to implement them. It was pretty daunting but the placements were supposed to help; unfortunately, mine it seemed was not exactly what I needed. All my classmates lived nearby so they all bagged the local assignments. I however, being from the sticks, was sent up north to help at the Uni. None of *that* seemed logical. "It's closer for you." No, it wasn't. Mileage-wise perhaps but it took slightly longer on the bus. *And* of course it wasn't a business, how was *that* supposed to help?

"You just ran out of placements, didn't ya?"

"Umm."

"Alright! Tell me straight!"

So, after three months theory, I was off to University. I'd considered it at school but couldn't stand those student types. I was just a rural lad who liked punk rock and playing football. I was reasonably bright but didn't know what to do with it.

The first day was a little stressful, I was in a shirt and tie which only added to my discomfort, smart clothes didn't suit me at all. The bus ride seemed to take forever, stopping every minute or so, meandering through every village until at last we got to the Uni. Well, part of it at least, the place was spread all over town. Some of it was pretty old but mostly it was modern buildings. I was in the Computer Unit, just a stone's throw from the library, situated on a hill, with well-kept lawns to either side and a little hazel hedge at the front. The Head of the Department met me, quite an unassuming chap, he spoke quite softly, which relaxed me, maybe this place wasn't so bad? He also wondered why I was there, considering the aims of the course. "Well, no matter, here you are, so why not make the most of it?"

3

At home, things were changing fast, my elder sister was getting married and then she was off to live in Yorkshire, which I had mixed feelings about. I didn't like her fiancée much but it wasn't me who was marrying him and I was sharing a room with my brother so one of us could snaffle hers.

The wedding itself was quite an ordeal, I'd drank at least four cans of beer and by the time I was stood in the church I was desperate to urinate. The Yorkshire crew were still in the pub and I wished that *I'd* been in there too, so when at last they did appear I was rushing past the other way.

Back at home, it was chaos, swarms of strangers everywhere, clamouring for food and drink, rattling on about nothing at all. Soon enough I'd had enough, I changed my clothes and got out of there, ending up in the betting shop, the very first time I'd been through the door. It was crowded, being a Saturday, and right next to the Legion Club, so drunks were in and out non-stop, reeking of booze and stale tobacco. Naturally I knew them all, I lived in Trimley, which was small, you ran into everyone sooner or later, whether or not you wanted to.

There was a kiosk off to the right with betting cards on the opposite wall. All the other available space was plastered with the racing form. A TV screen sat up in a corner, shrouded in a haze of smoke. *What a dive*, I thought to myself. I coughed and grabbed a betting slip.

The next race was the 3:15. I found the relevant bits of form. I didn't know what to do with it. I needed a strategy of sorts. Tough, no time, I took a guess. Bobby's Lad at 20-1. He skated in by a good six lengths. The horses were a piece of piss!

That night I was well away, a local pub crawl had ensued and I ended up in a neighbouring village where two irascible punky types were messing around like a couple of schoolkids.

They were girls, they looked at me.

"Alright ladies?"

"*Ladies*? Ha!"

"Alright strumpets!"

"That's more like it!"

"So, wanna come to the pub?"

"The *pub*? Hey, we're just fifteen!"

"You sound as though you've had a few!"

"Just the one, a bottle of cider!"

"Must've been a pretty big one!"

Jennifer, the one who'd spoke, was wearing a scruffy-looking coat, decorated with studs and badges, some of my favourite bands on there. Her ears were pierced with silver studs, her hair was brown and wild and unkempt, she looked at me through glazy eyes and I smiled at the crazy little vixen.

She was wearing a home-made t-shirt.

"Wow, the Junkies!"

"Aye, y'like 'em?"

"Well, not only do I *like* 'em, I'll be *seeing* 'em Friday night!"

"Where?"

"In Boroughby, Rock Palladium."

Quick as a flash, she grabbed my arm. Next I knew I was stood in a parlour with two formidable-looking women.

"Who are *you*?" the younger one asked.

"Eric."

"Eric?"

"Eric Peagerm."

"*Peagerm*? What sort of name is *that*?"

"I dunno, the one I was born with!"

"Well, OK, I'm Jennifer's mam. What the hell do you want with her?"

"Nothing! She just dragged me in here!"
"And you *let* her?"
"Little option!"
"Guess what, ma, he's seeing the Junkies!"
"So?"
"Come on, ma, can I go?"
Hmm, I thought, I never asked her.
"Come on, ma! Please, ma, *pleeease!*"
Then the older lady spoke: "Is this a club you're slinking off to?"
"Yes."
"Where at?"
"Down in Boroughby."
"How ya getting there?"
"On the bus."
"And back?"
"Well, me dad's car, probs."
She stared at me with steel-grey eyes. Her hair was fine and short and white. I guessed it was the grandmother.
Jennifer still had hold of my arm. What the hell was I getting into? Ma, it seemed, had just one ear. I didn't know what to make of it.
"What if our Jen can't get in?"
"I'll see her safely back on the bus."
"You promise?"
"Aye, I'm a gentleman!"
"You're not, but alright, she can go.

4

The Uni was a hive of activity, the computer room especially. Lots of whirring, clanking and clicking. This was old school, tapes, the lot. The mainframe was an IBM, housed in a large array of cabinets, mostly along the southern wall, partially sunken into the hill. It was like those TV shows, everything seemed futuristic, spacious but incredibly busy, hard to know quite where to look. Everything was moving or flashing, reels of tape, jerking and spinning, blinking lights which never ceased, binary thoughts of an inanimate brain . . . printers and plotters rattling away, spewing forth a deluge of data, tapping or scribbling furiously while reams of paper fed their voracity. It was pretty cool in there despite the non-stop barrage of noise, the air con worked around the clock to make sure none of it overheated. Then of course there were the people, Operators ran the show, Sebastian Short was senior, in his forties, kind but serious. His understudy was Mark Molloy, a younger, slender, blonde-haired chap who was always dashing back and forth as if everything was incredibly urgent. Then there were the Junior Ops, a guy called Pete and a girl named Judy, they did all the menial tasks and therefore it was they who trained me. Pete the most, a stocky bloke who seemed to play a lot of Rugby, "character building" he'd insist as he munched his way through endless snacks.

The work itself was rather basic, changing tapes, watching printers, swapping ribbons, paper, cartridges, nothing you could describe as technical. Special consoles held the jobs, the staff and students had no peripherals, they would have to come to us to pick up any prints or plots. Those glowing screens were little portals, Pete explained how everything worked. Whenever you had to key an instruction, first you'd have to type 'SEN M', a simple term which told the computer that you were about to send it a message. Mostly to prioritise tasks. There was a window off to one side and occasionally a face would appear with a look of hope or expectation. Pete or Judy would skip on over and either furnish them with prints or negotiate with the eager ones to give their work a bump up the job queue. That was power, in a sense, but only relative to the job and I sensed these little interactions were the highlights of the day. Occasionally there was minor drama, the system would throw a hissy fit and a bunch of geeks would burst through the door and dart across to one of the consoles.

"Oooh! THAT should not have happened!"

"Curious, Roberts, curious indeed!"

Opinions were ten a penny.

Programmers. A different breed.

5

Friday night then came along. I met Jennifer on the bus. She looked the same as when I'd met her, a bit more war paint on perhaps.

Two acquaintances got on.

"This your girlfriend?"

"No, it's not!"

They got off again at Sedgeworth.

Jen just sat there, chuckling.

The Rock Palladium was rough, it had the look of an old bierkeller. Dark and dingy, quite foreboding. Somehow they let Jennifer in. It was pretty empty inside, a band was setting up on stage. Jen went off to find the bogs. I made my way towards the bar.

The first band was a decent one, they dressed in Clockwork Orange clobber. Jen however was not impressed and she asked if we could go outside. We necked our drinks and did just that. It was cold. Very cold. Jen just looked at me and shivered. I tucked her into my leather jacket.

I held her close. Very close. I didn't feel the need to speak. She pressed a cheek against my chest then slowly slid an arm around me. That felt good. Something stirred. "Oooh, hello there!" Jen remarked.

"Stop it!" I said, "you're just 15!"

"Well, tell *that* to Mr. Stiffy!"

Suddenly I felt uncomfortable. She was underage but I liked her. No-one else had wanted to come. I seemed to just fall into things. Girls had never liked me much, I rarely knew quite what to say, and so as yet I hadn't 'known' them except for a drunken fumbling or two.

The second band we both enjoyed, the Refugees from Northern Ireland. Hard and mean. Proper punk. The place was filling up by now. I had to usher Jen to the bar, I'd been there with my sister once and every time I'd left her alone some bloke had always pounced on her.

Finally it was time for the Junkies. Jen stood up and cheered them on. She had spirit, lots of it, if only she wasn't still at school. The band themselves were pretty good, they also dressed up Clockwork-style, the singer's face was covered in greasepaint, clown-like, with a big wide smile. I preferred their earlier stuff, much harder, faster, more intense, their new stuff sounded like a circus, fun, but not as energising. Still, they had some solid tunes and bashed them out efficiently. Not much action on the dancefloor, nevertheless, an adequate set.

Soon enough the show was over. It had been a curious one. Decent bands but a dubious atmosphere, maybe I hadn't been drunk enough? My Dad was parked up down the road, luckily as things turned out, as just as we had hit the street a gang of thugs, who'd been at the gig, began taunting us and then following us.

We jumped in the car. "Drive!" I said. My dad looked scared and hit the gas. Jen just sat there with a grin.

Damn, I thought. I was hooked.

6

Jen and I became an item. Nothing sexual, at first. Going to jail was not a priority, still, I liked her very much. I'd see her on a Friday night and most times we would go to a gig, usually in Peterslee, about 20 minutes away on the bus. There'd be me and Jen and Babs, her best mate who I'd met in the street, a cute little thing, troll-like, but a smart one and a bundle of fun. We'd hit the offy on arrival and take our cider up the park, and there we'd sit and drink and laugh before stumbling over to the gig. Which was always in the youthy, a big white building up on a hill, where local bands would meet and play and make what we thought was a glorious racket. One band had a record out, Upwrought, they were local heroes, they would play there twice a month and we'd dance around and jump about to songs we could actually play at home. It was great, all of it, a drunken, hilarious mess of a time, the punks would all meet up in the park and bond through drink and a love of music. LOUD music. Raw and angry. Few of the locals were impressed, we'd always have a tape deck there and blast out all the noisiest tunes.

Regular folk would come on over.

"What's that shit you're playing?" they'd ask.

"Fuckin' PUNK!"

"Well turn it down, or turn it OFF!"

"Fuck you, GRANDMA!"

Even the local kids disliked us, they were stroppy little twats, always taunting us from a distance, laughing, joking, throwing things. Once, they turned up with a gat gun and took potshots at us from the swings, until we chased them off, mob-style. We were knackered at the gig.

Afterwards I'd stay at Jen's, which was really her grandma's house, a puzzling arrangement since her parents lived just up the street and they all appeared to get along fine. She had a younger sister, Sue, who didn't live at either house, but seemed to alternate between them, it was all a little strange. Still, the place was nice and warm, the parlour had an open fire, the fridge and cupboards always full to see me safely through till morning. I'd be curled up on the couch and Jen would come for a midnight kiss, closely followed by her gran, who'd always grab her by the hair and roughly march her back upstairs.

Then, suddenly, *we* moved house. That one came right out of the blue. The new one only had two bedrooms, me and my brother were mortified. We had to share a room again. Couldn't we have an ounce of freedom? "You can *have* your freedom when you find a job and buy your own!"

It was sickening, I was mad. One night I got pretty drunk. I staggered home in a hell of a state, hanging onto garden fences. Then my back door key wouldn't work. I stood there banging in frustration. Finally this bloke appeared.

"Eric, you don't live here anymore!"

By this time I was back in college, more than halfway through the course. All my former classmates had changed, they'd all grown up a little, it seemed. Most had been thrown in at the deep end and most had coped quite admirably. Lucky them, I thought to myself. It felt like I'd been left behind.

I had a meeting with the tutor, quite a solemn-looking chap.

"My placement wasn't relevant!"

"I know, but it's all we had."

We were all due back quite soon.

"Can't you find me somewhere else?"

"Sorry, no, it's too late now."

He could hardly look at me.

7

Jen and I kept going to gigs, always on a Friday night. If there wasn't anything on we'd just play records and get drunk. The kissing turned to heavy petting, occasionally we'd genital grind, I made a mess of her on occasion but technically I was still a virgin.

Then one day she wasn't home, her gran had sent her off to town, to buy some shoes, allegedly, but four hours later she wasn't back. At 8 p.m. she got off the bus, she looked at me quite sheepishly.

"What happened?"

"Oh, I missed the bus."

"You must've missed a few of 'em!"

I let it go. Things progressed. Her mother got her on the pill. Still, I refused to shag her. Shit, she was just 15!

Then one night, back at home, I noticed something in my pubes. Little bits of grit, it seemed, dotted about, quite evenly. I tried to wash it out. No luck. What the hell was going on? I tried to take a closer look. The stuff seemed welded to the hairs.

Then something moved.

"Shit! What's *that*?"

It looked like legs. Fucking legs! It moved again, my body shook. It can't be, I thought, it fucking *can't* be!

Well, it was.

I was horrified. Get the bastards *off*! I thought.

That was easier said than done. They really didn't *want* to come off.

The grit, it seemed, was just the eggs, I got them off with a pair of scissors, but once I'd trimmed down every hair the lice themselves were still in evidence, clamped on tightly to the roots. I tried to snip them off. No joy. I only snipped off bits of flesh, and blood was hardly any deterrent, the little bastards loved the stuff!

I ran for the bus and headed to Jen's. It was late but I didn't care. I hammered away on the door in a frenzy. I was mad. *Really* mad.

Her mother answered, sounding annoyed.

"Hey! Hey! What's all *this*?"

"Let me friggin' well in!" I demanded. "*This* malarkey's not for the street!"

I stood there in the parlour with her mam and her gran both staring at me.

"Well, come on!"

I took a deep breath. "Well, your daughter's given me CRABS!"

"JENNN!!!" she screamed.

Down she came.

"What?"

"He says you've given him CRABS!"

"What? No way! I haven't got crabs!"

Her mother dragged her into the bathroom.

Somebody squealed.

Out they came.

"So? Where did *they* come from?"

"Must've been a toilet seat!"

"A *toilet seat*? Oh, fuck off!"

We ended up in the special clinic. Me and her. Separate slots. I'd agreed to forgive her if she just came clean about everything.

The doctor gave me a bottle of lotion, white stuff, and a few instructions. Then he wanted to swab my cock. "What for?" I asked.

"For other infections."

"But I never put it in!"

"In where?"

"You know, the girl's vagina!"

He just stood there, looking puzzled.

"Look," I said, "she's just 15!"

We ended up naked in the bedroom, all prepared to slap on the lotion. Everything seemed so unreal. *What a fucking state of affairs!*

We shaved each other then splashed it on, quite liberally, around the genitals. I got hard, naturally.

"Do around the back for me, will ya?"

That was it, I did her alright. First with the lotion, then the erection. I exploded within seconds. She'd been kneeling down on all fours.

Afterwards we sat on the bed. "Right then, tell me all about it."

"Where do I start?"

"Start with the last one and work your way right back to the first."

The last was pretty obvious, the trip to town to buy some shoes. She'd met a punk lad in the street and ended up shagging him back at his flat.

"Didn't you *say* you had a boyfriend?"

"Aye, but I said we hadn't *done* owt! He said that if you really liked me you'd have shagged me *way* before now!"

Then it got worse. There were others. Many others. *Dozens*, it seemed. All the way back to when she was twelve. I stopped her there, I couldn't take it.

Nevertheless I'd said I'd forgive her. I would always keep my word. I shuddered to think where it all began. I hadn't even met her father.

Still, everything settled down, the crabs were gone, like my virginity. I was never going to jail. No-one gave a damn about that. We shagged like animals, all the time, in the bedroom, out in the fields, down at the beach among the sand dunes. I was making up for lost time.

8

Soon enough I was back at the Uni. Everyone seemed pleased to see me. That was strange, I'd had the impression I'd almost been in the way last time. It wasn't so. Pete explained: "We like it when you ask us questions. That shows that you want to learn and contribute to our tight little team."

Even Judy spoke this time, before she'd hardly said a word.

"I was just preoccupied . . . boyfriend problems, plus exams."

Her and Pete were both at night school, studying for different things. She was after a good degree, he was doing some kind of diploma. Operating wasn't enough, they wanted to push themselves a little, which made perfect sense to me, as long as you knew in which direction.

Pete then sat me down one day.

"What do you want to *do* with your life?"

"I dunno, *this* is alright."

"Alright but it's not enough! Whaddya *love*?"

"Punk rock, mostly."

"*That*'s not gonna earn you a living!"

"No."

"Well, you're just 19. Plenty time to find a passion."

Then my time was up, it seemed. I passed the course and got a certificate. Not much use to me, in truth. I didn't feel prepared for anything. Off I went to join the dole queue, down in Twinage, an hour away. I'd walk there once a fortnight with Terry, an old schoolmate who also signed there. It was so disheartening, the jobs they had seemed out of reach, I didn't have the relevant skills and whatever unskilled work they had was snapped up almost immediately. I did get the occasional interview, none of which were of much use, I'd sit there frozen into my seat, no idea what to think or say. It all felt useless, Pete was right, I had to find a passion of sorts; drinking and fucking and going to gigs was never going to work *long*-term.

But I did it anyway, at just 19 it felt so good, my future seemed a long way off, I'd find a job, eventually. The gigs moved west to Fenny Hill, a scruffy little market town, upstairs in an old-but-welcoming pub with the punkiest jukebox I'd ever seen. The bands who played were mostly local, North-East bands, no records out, but everyone seemed really friendly, overflowing with chaotic energy. Negative Purge from up in the hills, Sex Abuse from Lancheston, the Dirty Slobs from Howton Springs, it soon became my second family. Jen had finally turned 16 and was doing all sorts with her hair: colouring, soaping, spiking it up, shaving the sides, whatever she fancied. I just had a scraggy mop but Jen was having none of it and attacked it with a pair of crimpers and suddenly I had a hairstyle. Clothes-wise she was much more old-school, leather skirts, studded wristbands, fishnet stockings, zippers, bum-flaps, kinky boots, she loved all that. She liked to shock, wherever she went, they'd often send her home from school, if not because of what she was wearing then always because of her bad behaviour. Meanwhile I'd been dressing down, developing a more grungy style, but way before grunge, with flannel shirts and baggy old cardigans, most second-hand. The pub was called The Old Queen's Head, my favourite gig was one of the first, some old schoolmates had formed a band: the Untrained, from Fishwick and Sedgeworth. They were great, they had us dancing, the headline band were amazing too, the Newtown Neurologists, southern boys, more seasoned but with a driving beat.

Back at home, life was boring, nothing to do, nowhere to go, the old pit villages were decaying, few of the younger folk had jobs. We'd hang out at the Community College, a leisure centre with a bar, not that we could afford much drink, we'd mostly lounge around in the games room, playing cards, shooting pool.

Toby Dodsworth was in charge, a portly lad who despised inactivity, "Come on, guys," he'd moan at us. "Get outside and *do* something!"

"Like what?"

"Have a football match!"

"Had one yesterday."

"Have one today!"

"We're sick of it!"

"The National Game?"

"Aye, it's rubbish! Jumpers for goalposts!"

"Ask Bill Dobbs to set up a friendly."

"What? Who with?"

"A*nyone*, Jesus!"

"Jesus wouldn't give us a game!"

"Oh, ha ha, you know what I mean!"

Bill Dobbs ran a local team, the Trimley and District Under-18s, but he had contacts, lots of them, and the next we knew we were playing a friendly, with semi-professionals, Burnham United. 11-a side, on the big pitch, white lines, nets, a referee, there was even a reasonable crowd, a Sunday morning in July. It was great, with more to come, those contacts came from far and wide and soon we were sat on a coach to Scotland to take on teams from a sporting academy. First we played the senior team, they demolished us, 10-1. Then we played the under-18s. Closer, but we lost 3-2. Finally it was the under-16s. After a struggle we won 2-1. Cheeky little twats they were. Some of our tackles were disturbing. Minor drama on the way back, we made a stop at Jedburgh Services, guess who else we saw in there? Only the bloody Kids From Flame! A cheesy show by any standard, still, we were pit-village lads and to come across *anyone* that well-known was something of a novelty. We mooned at them from the back of the coach and glad to say they mooned us back. Two of the guys and one of the girls. I almost liked the show after that.

Back in Trimley it was dead. Jen was on a training course. I'd still see quite a lot of her though sometimes it got rather fractious. I'd be questioning everything, whenever we kissed it lacked any passion. She'd be cramming mints in my mouth, claiming that they made you infertile.

"But I thought you were on the pill?"

"I am!"

"Is my breath *that* bad?"

Obviously. Nevertheless she brushed me off and the mints kept coming.

I was miserable and it showed, she kissed me like a cold, wet fish. Once, I slowly opened my eyes and caught her staring into space.

"Aren't you into this?" I asked.

"What?"

"Snogging."

"It's OK."

OK wasn't good enough. OK wasn't much at all.

I'd watch her putting on her make-up, kneeling down in front of the mirror. Little arse-cheeks up in the air. Oh, to hell with kissing, I thought. But even sex was lacking something, she would never go down on me, I tried it but she wasn't responsive, it would always end in an argument. Maybe she was bored with sex? Maybe she was bored with *me*? All she liked to do was drink, or listen to music, or go to gigs. We did have one last passionate screw, we'd been away to visit her cousin and coming back on the National Express we both got carried away in the back seat. I'd been gently stroking her thigh and her hand had drifted onto my crotch, and that was it, her knickers came down and I laid it into her there on the bus. We didn't give a damn who was watching, fellow passengers, lorry drivers, we were horny and didn't care and I slammed it into her till I was spent.

Then the whole thing fell apart, I was in her room one night, her gran had sent her off the shops and I was fiddling with her tape deck. One of the tapes looked slightly different, it was newer than the rest, I couldn't recall having seen it before, nothing written on the label. On it went, I heard Jens voice: *Alright, fella, Jennifer here.* Fella? I thought. Which one's this? Her cousin perhaps? No, it can't be. She went on to describe herself, the way she looked, the things she did, then all of a sudden I was mentioned. *Got a boyfriend,* WHAT A TIT! Which startled me. I was WHAT? Then I heard the front door slam. I stopped the tape and sat there waiting, getting angrier by the second.

In she came. "So I'm a *TIT*?"

She looked at me in shock and horror. "Whatcha doin' playing *that*?"

"Never mind, who's it for?"

"Just a penfriend."

"Just a *penfriend*?"

"Aye, so what? Can't I have one?"

"Sure," I said, "what ya *can't* do is go around telling folks I'm a TIT!"

"Sorry."

"Sorry? Are you *really*?"

"YES!"

"Guess what? Don't believe ya!"

"Well I am, I really am! Even though you shouldn't have played it! Are YOU sorry?"

"No, I'm not, I found out how you REALLY feel! What's the point of SEEIN' ya if you just think that I'm a TIT?"

And off I stormed, marching home, Trimley was two miles away but I wasn't waiting around for a bus, she might have came out after me.

The house was empty when I got back. 8 p.m. on a Saturday night. The phone then rang. It was her. I took the damn thing off the hook.

I lay on the bed and stared at the ceiling. Was I *really* a tit, I wondered. Sometimes, yes. Everyone was. Didn't need to *hear* it though.

A short time passed, I fell asleep. Then, something woke me up. Someone rapping at the door. I dragged myself to the top of the stairs.

"Eric! Eric! Let me in!" *Oh marvellous.* "I know you're *in* there! Look, I wanna *talk* to ya! Come on, Eric, let me *in!*"

No way, I thought. This was it. My girlfriend didn't even *like* me. What was there to talk about? I'd had enough of it. *All* of it.

She started yelling through the letterbox. "Come on, Eric, ANSWER me! Let me in, cos if ya don't, I PROMISE ya, I'll go to TERRY'S!"

Aye, I thought, *I BET* you will. *DO IT* then! See if I care!

I really didn't, not anymore.

Good luck, Terry. You can have her.

9

It was time for something else. I bought myself a cheap guitar. An electric one, of course. No acoustic crap for me. I got a little self-help guide which showed me all the basic chords. All I needed was an amp. I would have to ask my dad.

"Put it on yer Christmas list!"

"Haven't got one."

"Well then, *start* one!"

"That's the only thing I want!"

"Excellent, it won't take long!"

I was getting nowhere fast. We were only in September. Christmas was three months away.

"Plenty time to get some practice!"

Down at the Community College the dole queue lads were getting restless, often there'd be a minor scuffle, over nothing in particular.

Toby wasn't having it. "What do you guys wanna do?"

"Find a job!"

"Apart from that!"

"Whaddya mean?"

"With your *leisure* time!"

"Play more footie, but who with, the bloody season's started now! Everybody's in a league!"

"So? Why not start your own?"

We thought about it. Yeah, why not? Why not start a Sunday league? Most pubs had a darts team and a lot of them were into football. That was it. We organised. We got Bill and Toby to help and soon enough we had twelve teams: the Trimley and District Sunday League.

We started late but the league was small, we even had two cup competitions, all you needed was a sponsor, someone to supply the trophies. Barry Bates Construction was one, a Councillor, I think, was the other. Can't remember who sponsored the league, the chip shop perhaps, the place was a goldmine. We were sponsored by the College, they supplied us with a strip, a few new balls, a bucket and sponge, a first aid kit, the half-time oranges. Everyone was buzzing, it was such a boost, we had a focus, finally there was something to aim for, sporting glory, yes indeed!

T.C.C. we called ourselves, a potent mix of flair and guts, a lot of us were old schoolmates, we knew each other very well. We'd hit the gym on a Wednesday night and sharpen up our fitness levels, those of us who didn't have jobs would meet up in the afternoons and have a kick about down the rec.

I played with a geeky stoop, my teammates rarely mentioned it, the opposing team however would often assume I was a bit of a plank. Which worked to my advantage as initially they'd leave me alone, until I got the ball in space and lashed one in from 25 yards.

One of the lads was into punk, a tall, sturdy, Aryan type, not only was he a stout defender but also he could play the bass. He was two years younger than me.

"Wanna form a band?" I asked.

"Aye, why not?"

Why not indeed. Inspiration was everywhere.

And so we did. Me and Adam. We got Joey Scott on vocals, all we needed was a drummer, drummers were in short supply. Luckily, Sid, from the Untrained had a younger brother who played the drums and before that fateful year was over not only were we football stars but ZERO TALENT were in action! We would practise every week, in Grangeworth, at the drop-in centre. It was always free on Sundays, thus we'd pick the afternoons. It was pretty tiring after playing football in the mornings, then, humping all that gear from the car park into the practice hall. I got that amp as a Christmas present, Adam borrowed his from his brother, Joey's microphone went through it, what an awful racket we made! Still, we wrote a few good songs and Gutta kept a timely beat; we clearly weren't quite ready for gigs but the prospect of them kept us going.

Then, 1984, an Orwellian nightmare? Not in Trimley! I was gonna start a fanzine, I could even feature the band! I'd found a typewriter up in the loft which immediately got me thinking and soon I was dashing off interview questions and posting them out to my favourite bands.

Three replied, the smaller ones. Bigger bands would rarely bother. What did they need a fanzine for? Sales were healthy enough already. It bothered me to a certain extent. After all, we were punks. Weren't we all supposed to be equal? Maybe I'd imagined it?

It was fun though, cutting and pasting, I was master of the Pritt Stick, filling gaps with bits of waffle, gig reviews, random articles. All I needed was a name, I couldn't think, my mind went blank, the bloody thing was ready to go and I couldn't even dream up a title!

Eight Years After was all I could muster, eight years after the birth of punk. Not the most original name but the zine itself wasn't all that original. Oh well, it would have to do. Maybe I could sell a hundred? Maybe not, I didn't care. I blew my giro and printed them up.

10

Down the dole I'd reached a milestone, six whole months of unemployment. That meant I had qualified for a fully work-based Government Scheme.

"Whatcha got?"

"How about NACRO?"

"What's that?"

"Working with offenders."

"Nah."

"Care work?"

"Nah."

"Youth Leader?"

"What? Kids? Not on your nelly!"

They insisted, pick one or it may affect your claim to benefit. Damn, I thought. What do I do? I chose the one that was closest to home.

"Ah, young Peagerm, welcome!" It was Toby Dodsworth down at the school. Officially the Community College but it was just a school with facilities.

"Pupil, customer, footballer, now employee, we can't get rid of ya!"

"Love the place, we're joined at the hip. OK, tell me, what do I do?"

Supervise for the most part, making sure the kids were occupied, with sports and games, mostly evenings, which was great, the days were my own. Occasionally we'd man the kiosk, taking bookings for the squash courts, signing bits of equipment out, trying our best to resist the tuck shop. There were five of us in total, three guys and a couple o' gals. A united front against the juveniles. Youth Leader. Who'd have thought it?

Meanwhile I was selling zines, to mates and contacts through the post, the record shops in town would sell them, they were gone in no time at all. I didn't sell too many at gigs, the punters much preferred to buy beer, but that was OK, I did too, at least I felt a part of the scene.

The Old Queen's Head was still having shows, thankfully I didn't see Jen, the Palookas played there, that was intense, the bands were getting faster and faster. And I was venturing further afield; some weekends I'd scoot off to Tyneside, on the train to catch a gig, mostly at an old police station. That place was a hidden gem, I'd heard about it through the mail, it had the feel of a scruffy old squat but apparently it was owned by the council. There was a sign above the door: NO GLUE OR GLASS, which made good sense, it had some bogs but not a bar, a good-sized room at the top of some steps with the whole place covered in graffiti. First gig I attended was great, even though two bands never showed. This was pretty common for punk gigs, reasons why I'd never know. I guessed their lives were too chaotic: beer, drugs, broken down vans, girlfriend problems, missing members or maybe they just simply forgot? The clientele were mostly punks, studs and leather, scruffy headbands, except one guy who stood in the background snapping away with a posh-looking camera. He looked slightly out of place but everybody left him alone. That was just the way it was, the Gateshed Pig Sty, everyone welcome. Anyway, a cracking gig, The Feed played first, fast and furious; then, since two bands never showed, the Dirty Slobs leapt up on stage. They were messy, always were, but that was always part of their charm, they had a song about a botanist, one line claimed: "*he fucks plant pots!*" The Peptix were the last to play, one of my favourite bands at the time, they had some cracking records out so I knew the words to most of their songs. I'd met the guitarist in the pub, just across the road from the gig, he'd promised me an interview and scrawled his address on the back of a beer mat.

11

Supervising kids was a chore, the little twats would run us ragged; if they weren't destroying the furniture they'd be destroying each other instead. We'd calm them down with a threat of eviction, sometimes with a threat of violence, we could never follow through but we all came close on many occasions.

Little Sammy Smith was a nightmare, always picking on vulnerable kids. Idle threats would rarely work, his dad was a thug and everyone knew it.

Bribery was the only answer.

"Settle down and I'll buy you a Twix."

Well, not exactly *buy* you, but, y'know, all part of the job.

I got into table-tennis. First I played the solitary kids. They would sit there looking bored and thus I'd offer them a challenge. Some of them lacked confidence so I would simply have to be patient; I'd allow them to win a few points then just as they were catching up I'd hit them with a backhand spinner.

Competition was everywhere, especially in Sunday League, the first thing you would have to learn was how to ride a dangerous tackle. Often you would know it was coming and you'd just have to brace yourself, but sometimes it came out of the blue, a thigh-high drop-kick from behind. We were good though, T.C.C., we almost ran away with the league, that side just had a natural balance where everybody knew their role. A confident keeper, Johnny Parton, firm, decisive, helped you relax; a solid defence with roving full-backs, two big centre halves in between; a powerhouse duo in midfield, Mitchy Stokoe and Kenny Dowler, motivators, strong in tackle, winning the ball then driving forward. Up front we had Tommy Bryant, actually an excellent keeper but that's not where he wanted to play, his real desire was hitting the net. Like the rest of us, he was hungry, always ready to smash one in, but Tommy had something the rest of us hadn't, the widest neck you'd ever seen! Bullet headers were his forte, a decent cross and that was it, he'd hang in the air like a muscular statue and nut the ball as if he'd kicked it. Thus we'd always play with wingers, Vaughan Hemmersly out on the left, and me, usually wide on the right, our mission to terrorise defences. Being two-footed was the key, we both could cross or cut inside, the full-backs didn't know what to do and thus we'd often leave them trailing. We proceeded to win both cups, the first one being the trickiest, the opposition were playing a ringer, a skilful, speedy, semi-professional. It came down to penalties so I agreed to take the last one. *Surely it'll be done by then*, but no, I had to blast the winner.

We continued with the band. The Untrained would practise with us. Sid, being Gutta's brother, had been told about our free arrangement. They were far superior, we'd watch them, it was obvious, some people felt the *need* to play while others simply wanted to. Then, one day, my amp blew up, we sent it back to the shop for repair but, days later, the shop went bust and we were told we couldn't have access. It was all extremely frustrating, dealing with administrators, finally it was all too much and Gutta left to join the Untrained. Well, they were better than us, we weren't called Zero Talent for nothing. He'd improved, the rest of us hadn't. I began another zine.

Meanwhile it was now half-term, a trip was planned to Water Valley. Three of us would supervise, myself, Mick Ross and Janet Robson. Ninety minutes on a coach with forty-five unruly kids. All that noise was nauseating. No respite. It wasn't good.

Mick got off to pay the gateman. It took longer than expected. They were talking back and forth then started making little gestures.

Finally he got back on.

"What the hell was *that* about?"

"Tell ya later."

Hmm, I thought.

Something strange was going on.

The bus parked up, we all got off. Smaller kids latched onto Janet. Off they went to hit the rides. Mick and I just stood and watched them.

"Well, come on!"

"There was a discount."

"Group rates?"

"Aye."

"How much change?"

"Twenty quid."

"Does Toby know?"

"I doubt it."

"Right, let's have a drink!"

There was a bar right next to the restaurant, we just sat there winding down.

"Jesus," I sighed, "kids are a nightmare."

"You might have your own some day!"

Mick was a whole year younger than me, of average size but more athletic. If he ate a chocolate bar he'd have to run it off in the squash courts.

It surprised me that he drank.

"Everything in moderation."

Moderation, what was that? I was ready for the next one!

12

We were lucky in the end, though some bastard grassed us up our only crime was leaving the kids, not the drink or nicking the money.

Toby understood the drink.

"Why'd ya think that I didn't go!"

He never knew about the money. Just as well, we'd spent it all.

Punishment was a long time coming, meanwhile I just persevered, trying my best to manage the kids, making *some* attempt to be responsible. Only the summer break remained, six more weeks then that was it. Back to the dole queue, sweet release, but those six weeks were pretty testing.

Every village had a Playscheme, basically a shed on the rec, replete with various bits of equipment to keep the children off the streets. I was bundled off to Grangeworth, Mick just down the road to Colton. We were dumped there on our own with a set of keys and no protection.

Then one night I ran into Jen, at a gig at The Old Queens Head, she bounced around, laughing and joking, sporting a big, red spiked mohican. It was strange, we said hello but off she went to socialise; I simply sat there smiling at her, trying to process how I felt. Did I love her? Not at all. Did I hate her? No, not really. It had ended miserably but it was pretty good to be free. I was a fanzine writer now, a girl would only get in the way. Occasionally I missed the sex but mostly I could do without it.

Meanwhile it was a hike to the bogs. I finished up then set off back. On my way I noticed Jen was sat on the stairs with a couple of lads. I suddenly felt uncomfortable. The fact I did confused me a little. There was a door just off to the left. I opened it and slid on through.

It was very dark in there, I felt around and found the light switch. On it went, the place was a mess, a dumping ground for a load of old junk with little space to move around in. Lots of chairs, a table or two, some of which were covered in dust sheets, pots of paint, some picture frames and various random bits of wood. Then I spied a can of adhesive. Ah, glue! People sniffed that! Wonder what they got from it? Curiosity overtook me. I unscrewed the metal cap and took a good, long hit of the stuff. Next I knew I was flat on the floor, drowning in a pool of vomit. Nausea would hardly describe it, this was more a dance with death, my brain was throbbing against my skull, my throat and stomach burning and wretching. I just lay there, hanging on. *What a way to go*, I thought.

PUNKER DIES IN SORDID GLUE BINGE.
"WHAT A TIT!" SAYS RECENT GIRLFRIEND.

Fortunately I survived, no doubt I had lost some brain cells, meanwhile I was terrorised by a bunch of rowdy Grangeworth kids. They'd been pretty nice at first, gently teasing, testing me, but soon enough they were running riot, whacking one another with cricket stumps. The McCauley twins were the worst, a couple of twelve-year-old ginger demons, always looking for ways to torture, ominous grins on their sick little faces. They would grab a skipping rope and tie each end to the frame of their bikes and then ride around the field with impunity, using the rope as a mobile tripwire.

There was a first aid kit in the shed, I'd have to use it every day, in combination with bottled water, for cuts and scrapes, all kinds of injuries. Still, Grangeworth kids were tough, I'd dress their wounds without complaint, a three-year-old got hit on the head, with a *cricket* ball, he hardly felt it.

Every day was full of stress. It was hard to watch them all, I focussed on the wayward ones, or tried to, there were quite a few of them. One day something caught my eye, the McCauley twins, way off in the distance, slowly heading towards the woods with a kid between them, half their size.

I sprinted off and caught them up.

"Where the hell do you think YOU'RE going!"

"Off to have a go on the rope swing."

"Not with THIS little one, you're not!"

I got pretty sick of it all, a few weeks in I'd had enough, I needed to keep them ALL engaged . . . group games was the obvious answer. First I got them playing football, it was worse than Sunday League, the ball was almost incidental, smaller kids got kicked to bits! I needed something more inclusive, softball maybe, and it worked, the girls all thought of it as rounders, it was baseball to the boys. One day *everyone* was playing, the boys, the girls, a mam or two, 'twas all good natured, lots of fun and I really felt a sense of achievement.

"Glorious stuff!"

A voice behind me. Ah, that was Toby Dodsworth. I just turned and smiled at him.

"Piece of cake!"

Of course it was.

13

Then, it was back to the dole. I continued with the zine. Jobs were still eluding me although I was applying daily. Admin work had been suggested. I applied to County Hall. I even got an interview, but what an excruciating experience. It was in a big, old room at the end of a long, mahogany table, populated with all these faces, staring at me, unflinchingly. Different people asked the questions. No idea who they were. The whole thing seemed a tad excessive. Didn't they have any work to do?

Meanwhile there was a miners strike, Thatcher was taking on the unions, many of my mates weren't working, even though they did have jobs. Jenson was a striking miner, like myself he liked his booze, but having lost a steady wage he rarely had the funds for drink. Luckily, a mate of his had a brother who ran a market stall, a stall that sold a lot of fruit, and since that could be used to make cider he asked if he could nip across and skim off any damaged items, focussing on apples and pears, anything bruised or overripe, it was strange how much there was but Jenson simply smiled and took it. Thus his house became a brewery, lots of us were willing to help, community spirit was never as strong as when there was alcohol involved. We scrounged around for a few old buckets and sterilised them thoroughly, or as thoroughly as we could, it's not as if we had proper chemicals. All that fruit then had to be pulped, it was the juice that we required, not an easy task, believe me, so the riper it was the better. We employed all kinds of methodology, hammers, presses, blocks of wood; we bashed that fruit until exhausted then strained the juice through a muslin cloth, or an old net curtain, whatever we had. The airing cupboard was always crammed with big old buckets, fizzing away, the results would vary wildly in taste, but so what, it was alcohol, right? The perry usually trumped the cider, it was sweeter, went down better, except one batch which got infected and slung out onto the wash-house roof. A few weeks later the roof was transformed into what appeared to be an alien landscape, weird, furry, fungal growths and to think we might have drank the stuff!

I did make the occasional gig, the Subnormals thrashed one out at the Pig Sty, they were good but it peeved me that they hadn't replied to the mail I'd sent. At least three times I'd sent them questions, always with an S.A.E., but no reply, for any of us, a few other zines had done the same. I could have grilled them but I didn't. What was the point? What could they say? Far too busy, far too lazy? Nothing would have satisfied me. The major press had no such problems, they'd obliged when *they* came running, and what were they doing with our stamps? Most of us were on the dole!

A solution was found for the stamps. Soaping them. Ingenious! All you needed was a cloth and the postmarks could be wiped away. Soon, everyone was at it. SOAP THE STAMPS! the rallying cry. Recycling for the impoverished masses.

ANARCHY!

CHAOS!

SCREW ROYAL MAIL!

14

Royal Mail had its uses though, not only did it keep us connected but I got friendly with the postman, soon he was throwing work my way. Cash in hand, delivering leaflets, he resented the extra weight and dealing with them slowed him down so I'd oblige whenever needed.

I unleashed the zine before Christmas, slightly better than the first, I tried to expand on soaping stamps, suggesting sellotape could be used. I paid for it with leaflet money, Ben the postie was always around, dropping them off, almost weekly, sometimes paying me in advance.

The new year quickly came and went, followed by my 21st birthday, I got drunk and ran around yelling 'No Time To Be 21' by The Adverbs. I was hassled by the dole, I'd hit the mark for another damn scheme and though I knew my options were limited I'd assumed there was more than one. Not so, there was only NACRO, which meant working with offenders, not the most appealing of things but if they had a space for you then it was pretty hard to refuse. Terry had done his time there once, he managed to put my mind at ease, he told me all about it as we made our regular trek to sign on.

"It's not too bad, there's nothing to it, couple of Jack the Lads, that's all. They teach you one or two basic skills and at least it keeps the dole off yer back."

As he spoke the heavens opened. We were unlucky with the weather. If we'd had our top coats on there would've been a minor heatwave.

There were different forms of training, painting and decorating was one, recycling furniture was another, or you could work on the nature reserve. Sadly I was put on the gardens, most new folk were dumped there first, then if you showed a bit of initiative you'd be promoted whenever they could.

A van would drop you off on a morning, mostly in groups of three or four, with rakes and spades and a roll of bin bags, usually at a pensioner's place. You'd be hoping it would rain so you could spend all day at the depot, tidying up or cleaning the tools, but mostly sitting around playing cards.

I was always teamed with Tommo, quite a vicious-looking chap, with scars, tattoos and a bad reputation, friendly enough but a bit of a psycho. "Come on over Twinage," he'd say, "we'll sink a few and duff ya up!"

"Charming, that's supposed to be fun?"

"Aye, for *us*!"

I'd always decline.

He'd be rolling fags all day while the rest of us got on with the work, combing through his greasy hair as if he thought he was terribly handsome. One day we had shears to hand, the garden was awfully overgrown and Tommo was sat there puffing away while me and this other guy hacked our way through it.

"You can help if you want!" I said.

He looked at me with his cold, dark eyes. I sensed I'd overstepped the mark but, for the moment, his mouth stayed shut. Eventually he grabbed some shears and occasionally he'd take a snip, then look towards me, moving closer, seeing if I'd edge away. I stood my ground. Well, I had to, weaknesses were not allowed, I did feel nervous underneath but outwardly I gave him nothing. Then, at once, a toad appeared, stumbling through the undergrowth, a big one, brown and covered in warts, bulbous copper eyes protruding. Quick as a flash, Tommo spied it and sliced the poor thing clean in two, then looked across for my reaction. I just stood there, horrified.

"Big'un," he told me, "you're too soft!"

Sure I was, I should've smacked him. I was almost six-foot three but violence wasn't any answer. Fisticuffs would not have solved it, education was the key, but you could hardly reason with a callous, vicious, cruel ex-con.

I had a word with one of the bosses. "Get me off the gardens!" I begged.

"Not just now, hang on in there, show him there's a better way!"

I was lucky in the end, a decorator had fucked up badly, papering a whole front room with a flower design all upside down.

"Maybe they were hanging flowers?"

"They were fuckin' *sunflowers* mate!"

Oh well, we were swapping places, best not make the same mistake.

15

I was not a decorator. Wasn't quite sure *what* I was. Though I learned a few new skills, in general, I found it boring. I continued doing zines, the next one featured the Untrained, I'd cornered them at a practice session and snagged an interview face to face.

By this time it was 9 years after and thus I had to change the name, I also changed the size of it, from A4 to A5, making it cheaper. Some of the pages were pretty rough, I brought it up with the video man. His main pursuit was renting videos, photocopying was a sideline.

"How's about a tenner refund?"

"Aren't you gonna do it again?"

"I could, or I can give you a tenner."

Hmm, right. I took the cash.

Gigs were coming thick and fast, a couple of coach trips with the Untrained, a couple down in Fenny Hill, a few exuberant ones at the Pig Sty. Toxic Refunds played at both, an amazingly tight American band, and though I never spoke to them I did decide to look further afield and the next zine featured a band from Tulsa.

Then I was recycling furniture, you were doubled up in a van and off you'd go to exotic places, collecting stuff or dropping it off. Most of it was gnarled old tat, functional but little more, the good stuff seemed to get diverted, mostly to the second-hand shop.

The driver's name was Colin Wood, a chunky chap with a dark complexion, always stopping off at the bookies to distribute his ill-gotten gains. He would never, ever win, he'd scream and curse throughout the day.

"HOW THE FUCK DID THAT HORSE WIN?"

It ran the fastest, obviously.

I asked about the 'good stuff' racket.

"What? You wanna BLACKMAIL me?"

"I just wondered how it works. Isn't everything logged at the depot?"

Yes it was, the bosses knew, he said I'd have to keep it shut. Just to be sure, the very next week, I found myself at the nature reserve.

The boss there was a decent bloke, up front with me from the very start. "Behave yourself and we'll get along fine."

That was all I ever asked.

We mended fences, laid some paths, did a bit of digging or strimming, then if it started pissing down we'd sit in the cabin, playing cards. North-East weather was unpredictable, sunny one minute, raining the next, the previous week, while out in the van, it had *snowed* in the middle of June! OK, we were up in the hills, but it was glorious back at base, an hour later our teeth were chattering as we sat there in our t-shirts.

Meanwhile I was learning to drive, a couple of hours a week with dad, a gentle fellow, once a miner, now caught up in quality assurance. It was pretty daunting at first, even on the industrial estate, but once I'd sorted out the clutch then things became more natural.

Eventually I sat the test. I had never been so nervous. The examiner was fierce. "What's that L-PLATE doing THERE?"

It was taped up on the windscreen, in the corner, out of the way.

"Well, it doesn't block my vision."

"No, but it DOES block MINE!"

I was forced to move the thing. It refused to stick to the bonnet.

"What am I supposed to do?"

"Tie it to the grille," he said.

Great, what with? I checked the car. Glove compartment AND the boot. Nothing. Nada. Fucking NIL. I had to think of something, fast. A shoelace? Yes! But which one? The right one or the left? Dunno. Think, man, think. I *couldn't* think! I yanked one out and got to work.

Naturally, I failed the test. I was simply *way* too stressed. The very fact I hadn't crashed, in a fair world, should have been enough. Of course the damn thing wasn't fair and pretty soon I was back on the dole. My new advisor sat there sighing.

"Come on then, let's sort you out."

She made a list of all my skills. "Alright, what have you done since school?"

"Youth Leader."

"What did you learn?"

"I have the patience of a saint!"

"NACRO then, what about there?"

"I can dig, strim, scythe; hang wallpaper the right way up. Keep my mouth shut when required."

None of this was any help, I didn't feel prepared for anything, I was pretty quick to learn but where were the jobs I *wanted* to do? I couldn't even hold a baby, my sister had recently given birth, but holding her felt almost alien, nothing seemed to work for me.

16

Ben kept coming with the leaflets, hardly a career, but still. All that cash in hand was useful, going to gigs, printing zines. I was getting letters from everywhere, faithful readers, one and all. Trading tapes, swapping stories, some of which were pretty colourful.

Then I got an invitation: "Come on down and see the South!"

Seen it, I thought, but what the hell. Everybody needed a holiday.

This guy said he made home brew, that alone was quite appealing, said he'd meet me up in London, catch a gig then head to his. He seemed pretty boisterous, he swore a lot in all his letters.

"I don't mind you Geordie CUNTS!"

Praise indeed.

Off I went.

The gig was tucked away in Greenwich, local punks, Rubella Ballot, known for wearing dayglo clothes but still a pretty solid combo. Everything was D.I.Y., the clothes, the records, how it should be, fuck big business, all of it, the kids could do it on their own. Mutt meanwhile, my new companion, seemed averse to sitting still, he was up and down non-stop, dashing back and forth like a pinball. He'd located two of the band, Zid and Sillah, friendly people, thus an interview began, followed by a cracking gig.

We arrived at his next morning, some old town along the coast, the living room wall was covered with beer cans, empty but a sight to behold. The home brew wasn't strictly ready but so what it was almost there and once we'd had some kip and eaten, two pint pots were dipped right in.

It was awful. Fucking awful. "Conkers in vinegar!" I suggested. "Didn't you sterilise the bucket?"

"Nah. Scrubbed it out, that's all!"

I got it down, a couple of pints. Then I went to go for a piss. Next I knew I fell arse over tit and almost brought the couch down on top of me.

Back at home, life continued. Sunday League had started again, with 20 teams, some quite good, the whole thing felt much more competitive. Then I thought about the next zine, how about a yellow cover? Zid and Sillah had inspired me, why not add a bit of colour? I decided to get them printed, cheaper than the photocopier, halftone photos, decent paper, the results were far superior. They were sold in North America, Finland, Germany, Italy, Spain, a few of them had made it to Poland, Czechoslovakia, Yugoslavia. Gigs were still quite problematic, everyone preferred the booze, I'd mooch around with a worn old carrier, soaking up the same excuses. Then, a friendly lad on Tyneside offered to help me out one night, and off he went, happily mingling, sold the lot in half an hour. Clearly it was me, I thought, I didn't have the powers of persuasion, didn't have the gift of the gab, I couldn't sell things face to face. That was why I'd failed at interviews, couldn't even sell myself, my people skills were sadly lacking, even in a room full of punks.

Gigs around that time were amazing, especially bands from overseas, they seemed exotic, nuanced, different, raucous as any but with a twist. I'd seen the mighty Wretch Head on Wearside, touring with the Cider Punx, a thrashy, messy, glorious evening, god knows how I made it home. I was back again in the Autumn for D.O.8, the Canadian band, but this time I was completely mortal, couldn't remember a fucking thing. I was making my own home brew, double the sugar, the punk rock way and by the time I was stood in the queue the alcohol had swamped my brain. I woke up on a bowling green, face down in the morning dew, zero memory of the gig, no idea if I'd even got in! I staggered around, completely lost, hardly anyone out on the streets, until at last I found a milkman who stood there laughing and shaking his head before furnishing me with a bottle of orange and packing me off to the bus depot. It was a Sunday. Nothing running. I was due on the pitch at ten. I bit the bullet and found a phone box. Dad was there by 9 a.m.

I made the match but didn't play, I simply sat on the sidelines, puking, I was in a terrible state, my brain and stomach couldn't cope. Still, I'd somehow made a friend, a few days later I got a phone call, one of my readers from Manchester, who said we'd met before the gig.

Apparently he'd got me a ticket, for the mighty Who Skidoo.

"Where?"

"At the Happy Ender."

"Really?"

"Yes."

"See ya there!"

The Happy Ender, that was famous, mostly they had indie bands but Who Skidoo were something else, the music papers worshipped them.

And off I went, on the train, bag of fanzines, more home brew, a cracking gig from what I remember, I was thoroughly soaked in sweat. I fought my way to the back of the room and ended up in the street outside, where suddenly things became confusing, couldn't remember where I was.

I saw a phone box down the street. Next I knew I was dialling home.

"Dad?"

"*What?*"

"Come and get me!"

"*Where you at?*"

"London, I think!"

"*London?*"

"Aye."

"*Are you sure? Thought you were in Manchester?*"

I thought about it. "Oh, that's right!"

I heard him slam the phone back down.

Then another gig on Wearside, suddenly I was back at The Shelter, somehow the Butthole Servers were playing, a legendary band from Texas.

I was one of the first ones in, cassette deck ready, Scoop McCann. This was gonna be great for the zine, a whacked-out, crazy, improvised interview. Sure it was. Though I spied them, just as they were walking in, the minute I got the microphone out the singer assaulted me with gibberish.

"Away, foul Fancor, scatter thy demons! Cease and desist, oh Targ of depravity! Fornicate with slop at will, but thrust at me thine prong no more!"

Anyway, the gig was great, a crescendo of noise and drug-fuelled insanity. I just stood there, mesmerised, I'd not seen anything *close* to that. Afterwards I slept upstairs, across a row of old wooden chairs. Many were allowed to stay. The Shelter was a friendly place.

17

Then, something unexpected, Ben the postie came a-knocking. Not with any leaflets but a more substantial proposition.

"How'd ya like to work for us?"

"Officially?"

"Aye, as temp. We already have a regular guy but it seems he needs an operation."

Right, I thought, a foot in the door, at last, a little sliver of light. I accepted immediately. Didn't even need an interview. I could simply bide my time, I'd soon replace the regular guy and then, when someone died or retired, I'd shuffle in and be set for life!

The sorting office was down in Statton, half an hour's walk away. It wasn't easy getting up but the journey always cleared my head. There were five of them in there with a supervisor in the corner, they all helped me sort my mail until I got the hang of things.

Our domain was pretty small, five walks covering four small villages, two in Trimley, much the largest, plus a rural route for the van. It was easy for the most part, strolling through the streets at leisure, sliding all that mail through the doors, the only drawback being the weather.

Kenny, who would drive the van, would drop me off at the start of my walk. "There you go, young man," he'd say before disappearing into the distance. I would strap my pouches on then stride off getting down to business, steadily reducing the load until at last my bags were empty.

Whether or not I had to return depended on which walk I had, the full-time walks had a second delivery, the part-time walk and the van did not. I'd have to come back on the bus, or walk back if I had the time, the villages were quite close-knit so either way was viable.

The situation down the dole was puzzling to say the least, with temporary, occasional work they couldn't agree on what to do. Sometimes they would sign me off, at others I'd declare my earnings. I'd have liked consistency but somehow I would never get it.

There was extra work one Saturday, two of them were off to Wembley, one of the local teams were playing, a team that I'd supported myself. It did mean doing two whole walks so everybody got a delivery, still, it was twice the pay and I made it home by 2 p.m.

I watched the match with much home brew and everybody barred from the living room. It was dire, my team were crap and I must have fell asleep near the end. I woke up desperate for a slash and as I stood there in the bog I thought about a mate of mine, a huge fan of a rival team. He was bound to take the piss so why not get in first, I thought. I finished up then got on the phone. His father answered: "*Can I help?*"

"Is Randy there?"

"*He's up in his bedroom. Just a sec, I'll go and get him.*"

"No, don't bother!"

"*Really? Why?*"

"I'm just so bloody angry, that's all!"

"*What about?*"

"Hasn't he said? He's only got me sister pregnant!"

"*What, our Randall?*"

"Aye, that's him! Randy by name and randy by nature!"

18

I continued with the zine, eventually it was 10 Years After. I was getting a thousand done and each one had a colour cover. It was quite a daunting task, the pages had to be folded, stapled, the bedroom was awash with paper, sometimes it was hard to get in. How was I shifting a thousand copies? It was pretty hard to believe, the mail kept pouring in each day, much of it from overseas. It felt like I was part of something, an independent global network, based on trust and a shared passion with lots of people just like me.

I also started selling records, sometimes I would trade for them, the records always sold much faster and helped the rapid spread of the zine. Yes. Records. That was next, or I could do a flexi-disc. The Untrained had done a demo, I could make a disc of that!

So I did. It was easy. All you had to do was ask.

"How do you make a flexi-disc?"

Someone always gave the answer.

Like that Desolate Bicycles song, one of the greatest ever recorded, a lo-fi blast of inspiration, "IT'S EASY AND IT'S CHEAP, GO AND DO IT!"

And it was!

Still, cheap was a relative term, I had to double the price of the zine, but 50p was cheap enough, half the price of the average single. Opinion on the disc was divided: decent songs but a little lightweight. Objectively I had to agree. Still, the Untrained were better than that.

I was in demand at home, by now I was the home brew meister, it would never last too long, there was always someone at the door. I tried it all, I loved the beers, the stout was really something, but the barley wine, that stuff was rocket fuel, got you where you wanted, fast. Five of us were on it one night and then we staggered off to Grangeworth, stoppy-backs in a local hostelry, pool and cards well into the night. Terry felt he couldn't make it, falling sideways into the road. He lay on his back, unable to move. "I'm fucked!" he said. We had to leave him.

I was biggest mates with Terry, often it was just us two, we schooled together, walked to the dole, he was actually born the day before me. Though I was tall, he was short, and cheeky with it, not like me, which made him pretty popular, although he took a punch or two. We went to many gigs together, some of which had been sold-out, but such constraints did not deter us, off we'd go on a wing and a prayer. Like Half Man Half Cake down in Stockby, drinking home-brew in the car park, bribing a bouncer to get in, a fiver for both us, that was inspiring. Off we went to the Mayday on Tyneside, Metal Mayhem and Axetrax were playing, not our usual kind of stuff but someone had told us they were great. A massive queue was stood outside, we sauntered past it, no-one cared, the bouncers seemed to have their hands full, little scuffles everywhere. We slithered in! Axetrax played, a mass of flailing, sweaty hair, especially in front of the stage, I almost lost a few front teeth! It did get very hot in there so stupidly we went outside, but then of course, lacking tickets, we were not allowed back in.

19

Jenson was a little older, looked as though he'd seen some things with broken teeth, lots of piercings, quite an assortment of tattoos. He seemed to do alright with the ladies, none of us could understand why, he didn't have any obvious charm but the girls were often mad for him. We followed him home one night from the pub, he had this hippie type in tow, we'd all decided to mess with them, myself, Terry, Ted and Hawkeye. We were huddled in the garden, just below the living room window, scratching on it, occasionally tapping, they'd be peering out through the curtains. This went on for quite a while, far more than was necessary, still, the bastards wouldn't come out, they wouldn't even open the window! Finally the rest got bored but I decided to persevere and woke up many hours later covered from head to toe in slugs.

Occasionally we went on road trips, gigs, festivals, punks picnics, sometimes we would visit Rob who'd just left home to go to Uni. They were fun, in Jenson's car, or maybe Ted's, it didn't matter, off we'd go in search of adventure, speeding down the motorway.

Sometimes Jenson would have drugs, once he had this pinkish powder. Coke, he said.

"Isn't that white?"

"PURE coke is."

Hmm, I thought.

"Give it here!"

He passed me some. I rubbed a little on my gums. They went numb. "Coke it is!"

At least a portion of it was.

He snorted it a few hours later and couldn't stop his eyes from watering. We all stood there pissing ourselves.

"Stick to fuckin' beer!" we said. He declined, his eyes got worse. "Look!" I said, "The poor bairn's crying!" He just laughed and did some more. We liked to think we had more sense.

Not that we were against all drugs, some were pretty entertaining and thus one Sunday, before the football, Jenson drove us out to the country to help him pick some magic mushrooms. Wasn't quite sure what they were but 'magic' sounded good to me and the next I knew we were stood in a cow field, rummaging through the grass for fungi.

"Whadda they look like?"

"Beige when dry. Sorta olive green when wet. Check for nipples."

"NIPPLES?"

"Aye. Pointy caps. Looks like a nipple."

Right. So I started searching.

"This one?"

"No."

"*This* one?"

"No."

"Why not?"

"Cos it fuckin' *isn't*! Far too yellow, stem's too straight!"

Eventually, Jenson found one.

"Right! Show me!"

And he did.

"Alright. Got it."

Shortly after we trundled home with loads of 'em.

That night we were sat in Terry's, me, him, Ted and Blondy. Jenson, being a ladies man, occasionally had other plans.

We shared the mushrooms equally, there must have been around 20 each.

"Whadda we do?"

"Eat 'em!"

"Raw?"

"Aye. Raw. Get 'em down ya!"

So I tried. They were foul. Mild at first then quite unpleasant.

"Where's the fuckin' sauce?" I demanded.

Terry obliged. Then we waited.

Soon, I began to feel strange . . . it was pretty hard to describe . . . just a general sense of uneasiness, butterflies around my stomach. The TV started sounding weird. I looked at Terry, he was smiling. So was Ted, he looked at me. He started laughing, as did Blondy.

Finally everyone was laughing.

"Eric, you're so fuckin' *ugly!*"

"Suck my nipple!"

More hilarity. Fortunately no-one tried.

Then I started getting the visuals, everything burst into life, the walls were heaving, objects moving, the carpet became a sea of colour! Terry's face looked really weird . . . he's a gnome, I thought, a *gnome!* A little gnome in a comfy chair. But hey! What's he done with his hat?

We ended up in the street outside, everything looked so dramatic, the scale of things, it all seemed *vast*, the lawns looked two foot deep in grass! The road was lit by shimmering floodlights, towering way above in the sky, and the wind, the wind, blowing forceful, somehow everything seemed alive!

It was great, I felt real joy, unlike anything I'd experienced, alcohol was lots of fun but it wasn't a patch on any of this! This was sensory overload and I embraced it, every minute, though time in general had no meaning, suddenly that was patently clear.

We wandered through the village, slowly, gazing up at things with wonder, every time we passed someone the four of us would burst out laughing. Off they'd go, glancing back with a look of sheer disgust or puzzlement. Well, so what, it didn't matter. Nothing mattered in the end.

We made it up the hill to the crossroads, where we stood in contemplation.

"Where to next?"

No suggestions. It was suddenly hard to think. Then I felt a few sensations, thirst was one, tiredness another. I'd been up since 6 a.m. Not to mention playing football.

There was a pub just down the road.

"How about The Falcon?" I said.

"Aye."

"OK."

So off we went, striding away in unison.

Suddenly it felt miles away, I didn't care, it was all downhill, a glowing tavern at the end, serving all that glorious ale. We marched along, smiling and laughing, loving life in this crazy world, the trees all waving, the footpath glittering, clomping down the yellow brick road!

Then I saw the bus shelter, almost halfway down the hill. That looks fuckin' *tiny*, I thought, I reckon I could jump the thing! And that was it, I started running, getting faster with each passing second, striding ahead, invincible, my entire structure as light as a feather. Immeasurable acceleration, I was defying gravity, physics, *this* is what they meant by magic, superhuman alchemy! Then all of a sudden everything changed, the shelter wasn't tiny no more, no longer was it just a hurdle, it was *huge* and made out of bricks! Time came swiftly into focus, I had possibly seconds to live so I swerved, violently, off to the left and went somersaulting into a hedge. The others simply stood there laughing. Strangely enough I didn't seem hurt, a little breathless and shocked perhaps but otherwise I felt just fine. The shelter stood there tall and foreboding. SHOW ME SOME RESPECT! it said. Not verbally, but well, y'know. Impossible, it stank of piss!

There was another outside The Falcon, a shadowy figure lurked inside. It was Jenson in a trenchcoat.

"Where ya off to?"

"Sedgeworth," he said.

Something moved inside his pocket, then he turned to face the wall. *What the fuck's he doing?* I thought. Suddenly an almighty BANG!!!

Off I went, over the fence, legging it like a startled deer or maybe an olympic athlete reacting to the starter's gun. I sprinted way across the field, scarcely taking a single breath, oblivious to *why* I was running, I only felt I needed to.

Then, at once, another fence. I hit the brakes and turned around. The Falcon sat way off in the distance, nothing there worth running from. I caught my breath and wandered over. Couldn't seem to open the door. Was it half-past ten already? Maybe. Didn't have a watch.

Then I thought I'd try the back. I stood there knocking on a window. Finally, it opened up. "Whaddya want?" Blondy asked.

"Whaddya think?"

"Use the door!"

"Can't, it's locked!"

"No it isn't!"

"Yes, it is! Pull me in!"

He stood there laughing. "Come on, dafty!"

So I reached, he grabbed my arms, I got one foot against the wall, I pushed, he pulled, I started moving, got my head and shoulders inside.

Then I suddenly ran out of energy.

"Pull!" I said.

"I fucking AM!"

He was, but only on my jumper, he was dragging it off my back.

"Come on!" he said.

"I can't, I'm weak!"

"Use your legs!"

"Haven't got none!"

I was stuck there, dangling.

They finally let me in through the door.

I stood at the hatch with a palm full of currency. Lots of people in the bar. Everyone was staring at me. Nick, the landlord, sauntered over.

"Whaddya want?"

"Pinta Best."

He brought it over. "Eighty-five."

I stood there looking at the coins. "How much is this?"

"Oh, for fuck's sake!"

But that pint of beer was fine. *More* than fine, *delicious* actually, I decided to savour it, just taking little sips now and then. The pool table was hypnotising, it was green, so very *green*, and all those balls, the colours, the numbers, no idea what anything meant.

Then all of a sudden Nick appeared with a huge tray full of Yorkshire puddings and all these little stoneware jugs which seemed to be overflowing with gravy. There was enough for everyone and we all just stood there, tucking in, with me, Terry, Ted and Blondy hugging a table in the corner.

"Mmmmmm!" I said.

"Nom nom nom!"

Terry started choking on his.

Everyone laughed, at least the four of us. Everyone else stood well away.

20

For me, punk was built on values: truth, respect, a sense of community; fuck the system, naturally, and whenever you can, D.I.Y. Not everybody felt this way, the scene did have its share of idiots, not to mention certain folk who simply seemed to defy all reason. One got 20 zines from me, he said he'd sell them, not a problem, then he sent a letter one day to inform me that his parents had burned them. Well, I thought, it could have happened, who was I to question things, but then his parents wouldn't pay and his wages weren't enough to refund me. I was frowning pretty hard, he'd hoped that we could still remain friends, but then he asked, without any shame, if I could send him the latest zine! Y'know, the new one with the flexi, he even included an S.A.E., I burned it of course, minus the stamp, and printed his crap in the following issue.

Then it was 11 Years After, issue 9, which proved contentious, almost exclusively down to the cover, drawn by Melly who had his own zine. I thought it was sharp and funny, ridiculing stereotypes, but many didn't get the joke and took the whole thing way too seriously.

Gigs were coming thick and fast, back I went to Manchester, the Dutch band B.G.A. were playing, I really didn't want to miss them. They were great, incredibly tight, they even had a fretless bass, the Electra Hippies provided support and as I prowled around the venue I got to talk to a number of folk that I'd previously met through the zine. I even sold the few that I had and bought some other publications, didn't find a crash pad though, the entire audience seemed to have travelled, I didn't meet a single local. I was forced to sleep at the station, or at least I attempted to, but no chance it was way too loud with drunkards, shady types and weirdos, screaming, shouting, clattering about. One guy seemed to be stroking himself while others simply stood and watched him. Jesus, I thought, what a menagerie! God knows what they thought of *me*.

The Pig Sty closed for safety reasons, still I often went to Tyneside, gigs were springing up all over, venues that I'd never heard of: the Angled Asian, Broken Moll, the River View on top of the stoop. Peep, who'd booked the Pig Sty shows, had moved a lot of the punk gigs there. Getting back was often a chore, especially if you went alone, you could get a train halfway but the last half meant a lift or a taxi. Failing that you'd have to walk, a good three hours in the dark. Usually on a Sunday morning, footie was insane after that.

All this action up on Tyneside shrunk the crowd at Fenny Hill, some excellent bands would come and play but often to an empty room. Post Moderne from down in Skeggy, German band Infernal Flame; hardly anyone turned up, the place was dying on its arse. Adam did attend some shows but mostly it was me and Terry. "Don't forget the brew!" he'd say. Of course not, we were on the dole! Though sometimes it could be destructive, once we never made the gig, we staggered through the city streets oblivious to our surroundings. Obviously we'd fucked up somewhere, we were only village lads, those streets all looked the same to us with little to distinguish them. Frustrated, Terry kicked a rock which sailed on through a plate glass window, triggering a piercing alarm which set us off in different directions. Flashbacks to the mushroom trip, a loud noise and you were off at a gallop, reacting as opposed to thinking, scattering in a state of panic. Not that I could run too far, I hid behind a wooden fence and stood there staring at a spider glistening in the light of the moon. That appeared to settle me but eventually I needed a piss, then afterwards I turned around to see exactly where I was. I seemed to be on top of the stoop, overlooking the river below, the ground was falling away beneath me, covered in a messy scrub. Though the lights looked quite majestic I was not at ease with heights so I edged along to the gap in the fence, the open road seemed far more appealing. Being drunk I didn't make it, tumbling down the slippery slope, though not too far, the scrub had brambles and all those briars slowed me down. Which stung a bit, despite the drink, but hey, I was still alive and eventually I crawled my way out of it, back to the safety of the pavement.

What a mess, I was covered in thorns, not to mention masses of mud. Not a look to be proud of though I'd have given the crusties a run for their money. The River View felt pretty close but I couldn't waltz in looking like that. Sod the gig I thought to myself. I decided to make my way back home.

I made an educated guess and headed off in search of the station, this I found quite easily so I sat behind the taxi rank and finished off the last of the brew. It was best to numb the pain. Mental, physical, didn't matter. I drained it off as fast as I could then made my way inside.

I sat there in the waiting room, plucking thorns from my fragile flesh, a couple of folks got up to leave while others simply tried to ignore me. Finally I caught a train but I was only half way home, the last bus, naturally, had left. I didn't fancy a ten-mile walk.

I found a phone box down the street and fumbled through my pockets for change. There wasn't much but it was enough. I slid a 10p into the slot.

"Hello? Dad?"

It started beeping . . . then went dead. What the fuck? I pressed the button to get my money back. Nothing. Hey, c'mon, you twat!

I tried again. Same damn thing. I was getting quite worked up. I only had one 10p left. Right. Better work *this* time!

It didn't, I was drunk and lost it, smashing the handset against the coin box, repeatedly, in a state of fury, hopping mad like never before. I was swearing like a trooper, cursing my luck, the phone, the world, my heart and soul and flesh all bleeding, I had lost all sense of control.

Then a hand upon my shoulder, next I knew I was sat in a cop car, ending up at the local station, stood in front of the Custody Officer. What a plight! What could I say? "Sorry, ossifer, I was drunk!" They knew that much, it didn't matter. Now I had to pay the price.

They searched me, which was quite an experience, I was wearing my special coat, a baggy German ex-army parka with two home-made compartments inside. One of them was full of fanzines, the other, empty home-brew bottles.

"Whatcha doing with all of these?"

"Recycling 'em! Whaddya think?"

Finally they took my statement and led me to a little cell. They tossed me out at 4 a.m. Didn't even get a breakfast. Bastards! I thought. Sunday morning. Not a bus till half-eleven. Had to walk it, badly hungover. Didn't make the footie that day.

21

Criminal damage, drunk and disorderly, that was what the charge sheet said. Wasn't sure what happened next but soon the coppers were at the door.

My mother answered. Shocked, of course.

"Eric! What the hell have you done!"

"Nothing."

"NOTHING?"

"Well, not much, a little worse for wear, that's all."

They offered me a simple caution, nothing to pay.

"Hey, that's good!"

Mam said, "Nothing good about it!"

It was more about the neighbours.

I was getting bored with the fanzine, all that folding, all that stapling, writing it was lots of fun but I didn't enjoy being swamped with paper. How about a record label? That seemed like the logical step. I'd already done a flexi and planned to do another one soon. Of course, it would take some work and I'd be swamped with records instead, but I was always receiving demos, maybe I could help a few bands?

The dole were hassling me again, I'd reached the mark for another damn scheme.

"Jesus Christ, I'm sick of your schemes! Where the hell have they ever got me?"

I was still doing postal work, declaring my earnings, what about that? A crappy scheme would get in the way. What were they trying to do to me?

Then it all fell into place, they told me about the Enterprise Scheme, they'd give me 40 quid a week to implement a business idea. Excellent, I had one of those, a record label with me as the boss! All I needed was a plan and a thousand quid to fund it all.

My cash was tied up in the zine but my dad agreed to give me a loan. The business plan seemed easy enough, press a bunch of records then sell them. Obviously it was more than that but I already had a decent network. I was shifting a thousand zines so why not shift a thousand E.P.s?

First band was a shoo-in, they'd already donated a track for the flexi, their latest tape was really good and I thought it might sit well on vinyl. Heavy Dissidents, from down south, loud and crusty but not quite metal, punchy with a political edge, we hadn't met but didn't need to. I just needed a studio, the flexi *and* E.P. needed mastering, cutting, splicing, all that stuff, preparing tapes for each of the pressing plants. Luckily I knew one of those, half an hour away in Stockby. Quick as a flash, I rang them up and got booked in the following Thursday.

Wow, I thought, a studio, so this is where the magic happens? It seemed pretty small to me but I guessed the majority of them were. Like the computer room at the Uni, it was jam-packed with equipment, although barely half the size and, for the moment, pretty quiet.

Stu, the engineer, was great, a fairly camp, flamboyant chap, with feathered hair, pure white jeans and a wildly exotic Hawaiian shirt. He didn't like the music much but it didn't matter, he was a pro, he asked me what I needed and I did my utmost to explain.

"Oooh," he said, "a brand new label!"

"Aye."

"Another Richard Bransom?"

"Well, not quite."

"I bloody hope not. Ugly bastard, that old git!"

I laughed, he was alright, Stu.

"Right, come on, let's sort you out!"

True to his word, he did just that and sent me home with a smile on my face.

I got myself a business account, a cheque book, cash card, quite the professional, I was officially self-employed with a nice little leg-up from the government. I suspected it wouldn't last but I planned to savour the whole experience, I was in my early twenties, who could say what lay ahead?

Someone mentioned S.R.P., a pressing plant from down in Cambridge; rang them up, a lady answered, very helpful and polite. I sent the tape by special delivery, phoned again to check they'd received it.

"Yes we have!" the lady told me, sounding quite enthusiastic.

"Would you like to come to the mastering?"

Would I like to come to what? That was something I'd never considered. Was I even interested?

"Is it really necessary?"

"No, no, not at all, it's just it's done at Abbey Road, a lot of clients like to visit."

I declined. Abbey Road. Legends had recorded there, but it was just a studio, no different to the one in Stockby.

Then more gigs, some in Brum, a van or a minibus picked us up, at first from a roundabout off the A1 as no-one knew where Trimley was! Shorn and Leppy ran the show, we shared a love of American bands, they'd both go on to form their own and still persist to this very day.

One of those gigs was almost a tragedy, Gan Green and the Circle Twerks, an incredible show, but near the end our good mate Ron, who'd been in the pit, came out insisting he'd been stabbed. It didn't *look* like he'd been stabbed, he sounded very nonchalant, until he pulled his t-shirt up to reveal an enormous gash in his left side. *Ouch!* That looked pretty painful, off we went to A&E, where everybody sat in the waiting room, drenched in sweat, still hyped from the gig. Terry took a bloody bandage and slung it hard against a wall. It stuck there in a bright-red halo. Everyone laughed. I mean, we *had* to. Thankfully it wasn't too serious, stitches, yes, but that's about all. Ron would yelp when the needle went in. Leppy sat there pissing himself. Next, the mighty V.R.I., the new E.P.s were ready by then, the sleeves not quite, it didn't matter, "Bring 'em down!" the Dissidents said. So I did. 50 copies. That was what I promised the bands. It wasn't a profit-making venture and everyone was fine with that. The band were selling them hand over fist, taking addresses to mail the sleeves later. That surprised me, warmed my heart. Glad that I was able to help.

22

Then the conclusion of the zine, 11 Years After, tenth and final, replete with a cracking 3-track flexi which even got some national airplay. John Peel blasted two of the tracks and followed with my contact details. I would often send him a zine, I got a fair few orders from that. I could've been in one of the bands, Bloody Thunder from up on Tyneside, Si was keen to switch to guitar and wondered if I'd try the drums. So I did, it didn't work, I wasn't all that good with my hands but my feet were useless with the pedals, it seemed that drumming was not for me.

The second E.P. was a band from Canada, they'd already been in the zine, a cool, inventive hardcore band, I supported an international scene. The first E.P. had a fold-out sleeve but Neighbourly Watch had no such needs so I thought I'd add a bit of colour and slip a lyric sheet inside.

I'd named the label Real Life Records, after a song by Who Skidoo, a song that really struck a chord and I hoped that I could do it justice. Be yourself, fuck the crowd, but try to keep it realistic, basic punk stuff, you'd have thought, but punks could be frustrating people.

Sometimes they would call me up. Once, at four o'clock in the morning.

"Hello, is that Real Life Records?"

"Yeah. You know what *time* it is?"

It was this American guy, oblivious to different time zones. It was strange, that oversight. Didn't they have them in America?

"Hey, where's your *accent*, man?"

"I tone it down for communication."

"Do you guys have *Christmas* there?"

Oh, Jesus Christ, I thought.

Then a couple of all-day gigs, one just down the coast in Scarton, one of the guys who'd organised it said he'd put me up for the night. Then Jenson and Terry decided to come and promptly got completely slaughtered, sleeping arrangements were revoked, it looked like we were stuck with the beach.

It was cold and wet that night and we struggled to come across anywhere decent, we just wandered around in a stupor, battered by the wind and rain. A couple of Yorkshire punks turned up, striding around, bold and boisterous, one was chubby with ginger hair, the other was tall and thin with dreadlocks.

"Ey up, lads, whatcha doin'?"

"Tryin' to find a place to sleep."

"There's a golf course up on the clifftop, just had a shit in the 18th hole!"

Eventually we found some huts, like bus stops overlooking the beach, replete with benches, wooden ones, *some* respite if still quite chilly. Off we went in search of firewood, couldn't find a fucking thing so we tore up one of the huts instead and somehow made it through the night.

Next a gig at Filer's Yard, an old brick building next to a river, the Untrained had played there once, the whole thing ended up in a riot. Me and Terry caught the bus and met with Boney at the station, one of his old NACRO mates, a surly type in a raggedy pit coat.

We were sat in a Greek café, wolfing down some non-Greek food, preparing ourselves to wash it down with lashings of home brew stashed in my carrier. Boney finished, then stood up. "That's me done," and off he went.

"Cheeky twat, he isn't paying!"

"Me neither!"

Terry left.

I was sat there like a lemon. *Jesus, what the hell do I do?* I wasn't paying for three whole meals but I guessed the staff assumed I was. I looked across behind the counter. None of them appeared to be watching. I could just get up and go. Nothing to it. *Come on, Eric.* Then I saw this enormous creature, standing in the opposite corner, carving meat, or something like it, expertly, from a vertical skewer. Shit, I thought, that could be me! My arse dropped out immediately. Maybe it was better to pay and sort it with the others later?

I just sat there mulling it over. Terry and Boney? Not a chance! They'd laugh at me, the pair of 'em. Fuck it, I thought. I'm not *that* soft! I got to my feet, slowly but surely, wiping my brow as I grabbed my bag, then carefully edged my way to the door while closely observing all three staff. One was serving, one was carving, one was dashing back and forth; I clenched my teeth and got the hell out of there, heading for the nearest toilet.

Filer's Yard was full to the brim, a mix of tribes from around the country, punks, hippies, crusties, suedeheads, still, everyone seemed friendly. Terry and Boney were stood there laughing. Yeah. Hilarious. *Fuck you too!* At least I got *some* kind of revenge, they didn't get a sip of home brew! I shared it with my new mate, Peace, a fairly eccentric type from the midlands, shaven head, a lot of mascara, like a skinhead Richey Manic. He was pretty manic too, he clearly had a few neuroses, still, I felt beneath it all he only wanted to make new friends. Despite his idiosyncrasies I'd rather have talked to folks like him than most of the human excrement that masqueraded behind normality. Curiously he'd heard of me, my reputation preceded me, but it was nice to have some company, Terry and Boney could screw themselves!

The bands played on . . . I got drunk . . . by 7 p.m. I was hungry again. I borrowed Peace's extravagant coat and made it up to the market square. I bought some chips and wolfed them down then stumbled past the taxi rank, which triggered something, ah, that's right! Jenson's do at Fenny Hill! A celebration down at the club, he'd said a few old mates would be there, some silly sod was getting married, but it was a party, what did I care?

Next I knew I was sat in a taxi, getting peculiar looks from the driver. Quite a fat bloke, gold-rimmed glasses. Friendly but uncomfortably so.

"Where ya off to, pet?" he asked.

"A party."

"*Really*? Fancy dress?"

"Not *this* time," I said. But *pet*? What the hell was he on about?

Then it clicked. It was the coat. Imitation ocelot. Quite a cheap one as it goes, but fetching if you were so inclined. It raised some eyebrows down at the club and thus I thought I'd milk it all. "You couldn't afford me!" I'd insist before flicking my head and flouncing away.

Jenson's girlfriend loved the thing. "Oooh, Eric! Gimmie gimmie!"

"Later," I said. I looked at Jenson. What the fuck was she doing with *him*?

I got a call from Peace next day, quite concerned about the coat. "Yes, it's here," I said, embarrassed. "Sorry mate, got carried away!"

I had to post it off to Mansfield, he was back at home by then. Poor lad must have been freezing, I thought. Still, sad to see it go.

23

Then onto the third E.P., a band from Scotland, The Perturbed. They had also been in the zine and I'd seen them live a couple of times. Not everyone in the band was keen, they didn't see the need for vinyl, which I thought was fair enough, cassettes were cheap and held more music.

"Can we do the sleeve AND label?"

"Course you can, whatever you like."

I trusted people way back then and hopefully they trusted me.

It was a blistering E.P., four great tracks of punk rock mayhem, they'd supplied a studio reel and a decent cassette so I could hear it. Excellent, I was ready to go, I didn't need the studio, I couldn't wait to get it out, I played those four tracks over and over. They'd requested a fold-out sleeve, with lyrics and artwork, like the first one, lyrics were so important to me, they let you know the soul of a band. OK, some preferred the sound and that alone could be inspiring, still, punk was more than that, the best stuff was a raging protest!

And I really loved the label, they had only sent me one, but what a concept, a punky flasher, the hole right where the cock should be! And to think I messed it up, the discs arrived before the sleeves but someone hadn't centred the labels. *What*? I was mortified!

I got on the phone immediately, the lady tried to be polite, but I was mad, I wanted answers. I was passed to the technical team.

"The bloody label's not been centred!"

"Sure it has, the *image* has!"

"It's the *hole* that's most important!"

"Really? Well, you should've said so!"

They refused to press it again; clearly it was all *my* fault, but lesson learned, if it's so important be damn sure that you spell it out! At least it was an excellent record which proved quite popular with the masses, no doubt I could have sold lots more but I was thinking of the next one.

I was trading like never before and each day brought a mountain of mail, from France, Germany, Italy, Poland, sometimes Japan or the U.S.A. I'd also trade in second-hand records, bolstering my own collection, I was inundated with wants and in exchange I'd receive old gems that I never even knew existed!

I had a special sack at the office. "Eric's!" they'd say as they tossed stuff in. They seemed quite pleased to see me down there, I felt like a celebrity.

"Our biggest customer!" they'd say.

"Really, at only six-foot three?"

Well, I spent a fortune on stamps, they'd clamped right down on soaping them.

Ben would pay me cash in hand, the rest went into the label account. That way it was more convenient, simplifying the daily cash flow. I'd experienced all the walks and got to know the quirks and pitfalls, no real perks to speak of but I got to hear some cracking tales.

Kenny, who would drop me off, would spread the gossip, when it was pertinent, who to watch, office politics, what was happening out on the streets. Not only did he serve the farms but he also did a parcel run, he knew the streets as well as anyone, no-one was a stranger to him. Short and stout with bulging eyes, he always had a mischievous grin, he saw the humour in everything so immediately I warmed to him. I mentioned a mate. "Yes, I know him! Called there with a parcel once! Nobody came so I tried the door and there he was on the living room carpet, wanking over a Woman's Weekly!"

Sex tales made me curious, I'd shunned it since the days of Jen, I had the desire but something inside insisted it wasn't worth the fuss. Kenny's sex life was something else, he had a wife and kids at home, but that didn't stop his lurid libido getting loose at every opportunity. He'd been shagging a local harlot, Dorothy James, a foul-mouthed sort, she hung around with her best mate Cynthia, drinking buddies who drank *a lot!* A mate of his had set him up, he'd carried her home from the pub one night and she'd promptly pissed all over his jacket before he could dump her on the doorstep.

Kenny knew: "A sure-fire shag!"

"Don't you worry about diseases?"

"No! Where from? Have you *seen* her? *I'm* the only one who'd shag her!"

Apparently, mid-hump one day, she'd yelled out: "MAKE ME YOUNG AGAIN!"

"I'm not a magician," Kenny insisted, "but here, have a bit more wand!"

Another time, mid-hump again, her mate came in with a pot of tea, then thrust her minge into Kenny's face. "So how's about seein' to THIS one next?"

24

Most weekends were spent in Boroughby, Jenson had just moved in with Ted. Jenson had fallen out with his family, Ted had a job at a mental facility. Often it was pubs and clubs but occasionally there might be a gig, the Rock Palladium perhaps or upstairs at the Plastic Pig. The mighty NoMemesNo played there, I couldn't believe it, they were fantastic, a quirky, driving, powerful, three-piece, shook your teeth, on tour from Canada. Talking of quirky, there was Shrub, reminded me of the early Fawl, with slightly whimsical tales of tomfoolery, amateurish but full of charm. Shrub were regulars at the Pig, even the Untrained played there, at least they tried to, sadly they'd been double booked with a wedding reception. One band travelled up from Batley, clearly they were not amused, we all tramped off to somewhere else, the Plastic Pig could go and get screwed!

Compensation for the Untrained, the following month I put out a single, S.R.P. were doing the sleeves, again, I was sick of folding. The sound was great compared to the flexi, crystal clear with much more power. I sent them all around the world, the mail poured in from everywhere.

Then it was time for the tax return, it didn't seem *too* complicated, money in, money out, all backed up with stubs and receipts. I spent a day completing the form and then bashed it off to the Inland Revenue. Didn't expect to pay any tax, it wasn't as if I was making a profit.

Meanwhile there were many road trips, I would hear about a gig, I'd mention it to Ted or Jenson and off we'd scarper on a whim. Maybe Planet Sex in Liverpool, or the Rock Spot down in Nottingham, often we would sleep in the car or just roam the streets till the driver was sober.

There was an all-day gig in Birmingham, bands from all around the globe, I met a few old zine folk there, it made me feel a tad nostalgic. Furthest we ever got was Glastonbury, that was such a nightmare drive, a good eight hours, including breaks, so glad I wasn't behind the wheel. Ted was in a Ford Cortina, Jenson had a 2CV, an upturned pram with a rickety engine, why, who knows, you'd have to ask. I almost missed the entire trip, turning up an hour late; I had some business at the bank but had to wait for it to open.

"Where ya been?"

"To the bank."

"Which one?"

"Does it really matter?"

"Aye, it does!"

"Alright, the *sperm* bank!"

"Making a withdrawal, huh?"

Then there was the queue to get in, a queue that never seemed to move. We sat there running out of fuel, sweltering in the afternoon sun. It was annoying. "Jesus Christ!!! Are we getting in or what?" Then Terry did a huge, wet fart. That was it, we threw him out.

Of course, once inside it was different, camping as far as the eye could see, a makeshift village in the centre, stalls and kiosks everywhere. We saw some bands, don't ask who, we dropped some acid, ate hash fudge, we braved the toilets when we had to and went home smelling like a sewer.

Then we did a few punks picnics, they were pretty much as they sounded, a gathering of punky types in the open air with a gig on afterwards. One was held on Cramond Island, that was in the Firth of Forth, the tide went out at certain times which meant that you could cross on foot. We all drove up in Jenson's car, the boot completely crammed with beer, we hadn't bothered bringing tents, we'd heard it was an all-night party. Yet another lengthy drive, not half as bad as Glastonbury, still, those roads seemed never-ending, squashed in like a tin of sardines.

Terry sat there looking smug, he'd bought a tray of Whit's White label. "None of that home brew for me! This lot only cost a fiver!" Righty ho, we sat there smiling. Everybody knew White Label. Yes, of course, it *was* real beer but the alcohol was one percent!

Meanwhile Sunday League was evolving, T.C.C. had broken up, I'd spent a season with The Stag, another pub, as centre forward. Not that I would score too many, frankly we were pretty poor and soon I was turning out for The Falcon, sadly not a great team either. Still, good lads who loved to play and occasionally showed flashes of brilliance; I scored four in a cup game once and was glorified in the local paper. We'd perform at some wonderful places, one was next to a huge ravine, we were always losing balls down there and had to pay some kids to retrieve them. Then of course there was Winstone Hospital, with a pitch inside the grounds, a psychiatric institution with many patients wandering free. One of them would hassle our keeper, begging him for cigarettes; she took a piss on the sidelines once, the whole thing was a bit distracting.

25

Then, it was back to E.P.s, a German band called Rotten Attitude, skate punks judging by the sleeve, whatever, sounded good to me. At last, Peely played a track, I'd sent him all my other releases but this was the first he'd ever played, I braced myself for all the orders.

What a disappointment, in the end I only got the one, I waited weeks but that was it, I found the whole thing quite perplexing. John Peel was an institution, surely millions heard his show, the flexi-zine had proved more popular, that surprised me enormously. He'd played the excellent opening track but the listeners clearly weren't impressed, I wondered why but that was futile, who could account for musical taste? Garbage often topped the charts while decent stuff could be neglected, still, this was Peely's show, I thought his audience had more taste! Maybe people liked the song but forgot to jot down my address, or maybe they'd just caught the title and asked for it at a record store? That approach would *not* have worked, my records weren't *in* record stores. Any enquiries would have been met with: "Rotten Attitude? Never heard of 'em!"

Right, I thought, a problem to solve. Time to do a bit of digging. I called a couple of other labels and asked them all about distribution. I was told about *The Alliance*, a union of independents, pooling what resources they had to get their releases into the shops. It sounded great, I called Red Lino, the nearest Alliance member to Trimley. I could get there easily, the guy said I should come and meet them.

"Bring a sample!"

What did he mean? Just the one or many more?

Next I knew I was sat on a train with 50 copies of each E.P.

I hauled them up the stairs to their offices, not too far from the central station, where I was met by a bright young thing who told me all about operations. Lenny Logan was his name, slim and blonde in a light-blue sweater; luminous eyes and a confident manner, exuding positivity.

Each E.P. was closely examined, front and back, inside and out. Not sure what he was looking for, I simply let him get on with it.

"Who's the pressing plant?"

"S.R.P."

Finally he'd scanned them all.

"Yes, I'm sure we can shift all these but remember we don't pay cash up front!"

Then, guess what? They went bust. I heard about it a few weeks later. After the initial shock I was contacted by the administrators. Chances were I'd lost my records. There was just no way to retrieve them. If and when the assets were sold I'd get a small percentage back.

It was depressing, though not skint I needed the cash for the next E.P., originally a North-East sampler but since just two of the bands had responded I thought I might go international. I had tracks by Neighbourly Watch and Rotten Attitude ready to go, a few other bands had sent me tapes so I booked some time in the studio.

Then I was hit with another bombshell, a tax demand from the Inland Revenue. It was over a thousand quid and I wasn't even making a profit!

I got on the phone immediately.

"Why the hell do I have to pay tax?"

"We have to tax you on your income. The drawings you made were quite significant."

"But the drawings aren't just income, some things have to be paid with cash!"

"Drawings are how you pay yourself, your tax commitments are based on that."

I'd been incredibly naive, I'd ran the label how I wanted, not how a business *should* be run, I'd simply been a bit offhand. I'd lumped the whole lot into the label, the Enterprise money, my Royal Mail pay, I should have kept the two things separate, Jen, it seemed, had got it right.

26

I agonised about what to do. Forge ahead or close the label. Closing it was easier but who the hell would I be without it? Money was needed to soldier on. I wasn't prepared to ask my dad. I owed him quite enough already and how would I convince the bank when the label was a non-profit venture?

Then I got a tape through the mail, a pretty eccentric sitar combo. What the actual fuck? I thought. I simply had to give them a call.

"Hi there, this is Real Life Records."

"Hi, this is Vishnu here!"

"You sent a tape."

"We did indeed!"

"But why?"

"To offer you our music!"

Turned out some old rockstar type had also started up a label. Focussing on 'world' music. *World* music. What was that? He'd also named it Real Life Records, hence the obvious confusion. How they'd dug up *my* address was much more difficult to determine.

Right, I thought, I'll sue the twat, I only needed a decent lawyer, if I won, the proceeds might have kept me going indefinitely. Rockstars couldn't just do what they wanted, they had *legal* obligations, just because I was small-time didn't mean I could be plagiarised!

I tried to ring this fucker up, I couldn't find him anywhere, no wonder I was getting tapes from deepest, darkest Hindustan! What if I was inundated, strangers turning up at the door, East African marimba bands or packs of Peruvians playing panpipes? No, I thought, I'm being silly, how much would a court case cost? Thousands at a minimum, those lawyers milked the system dry! Even if I won, what then? Maybe I could keep the name but compensation wasn't certain, how much had I actually lost?

Well, it had been diverting, time to drag myself back to reality. I just sat with my head in my hands . . . maybe I could rob a bank? Of course! *That* was realistic, Jesus, what was wrong with me? Other than the betting shop I couldn't think of anything useful.

Then, at last, a ray of light, one of the posties was retiring, Ben had turned up at the door and given me the official heads-up. If I could secure *that* job then maybe I could fund the label? It would be a lot of work but I was ready for the challenge.

I applied immediately and got myself an interview. I was working there already. What was there to think about? The other guy was unreliable, he had struggles with his health, whereas I was young and fit. The choice seemed pretty obvious.

What I didn't realise were all the little nuances. What you didn't tell them was as relevant as what you did. I mentioned I had A-levels, not only weren't they needed but they said an educated man might leave and get a better job.

"Anybody might!" I said.

"Yes, but *my* concern is *you*."

This was a question I needed to answer and evidently I had failed.

27

I was deflated. It was over. Reluctantly I closed the label. I decided to pay my debts and put the whole thing down to experience. There were one or two loose ends, the main one being the compilation, it was done and ready to go and I couldn't bear to let folks down. Thankfully, another label said that they'd release it, they were principled and honest chaps and said they really liked the music. I despatched the tape and artwork, told them what I'd promised the bands and out it came a few months later, just as I'd imagined it.

Debts? That was trickier, it took some time to sell my stock and when I found it wasn't enough I had to make a big decision. Sell a stack of records or be forced to put some debt on hold. No, I thought, I hated debt. Time to make a trip to Monkton.

Monkton had a second-hand shop, a little back-street enterprise, controlled by Fred, a music fiend who had a little flat above. He'd open up at 10 a.m. but get there any later and you'd often see that famous sign:

DON'T GO ANYWHERE
BACK IN A SEC!

Fred Behr was a local legend, helped me out on many occasions, probably helped hundreds out, his shop was always there for emergencies. He'd consume my unwanted records, not that they were always unwanted but since I'd never had a job I was always pretty short of cash.

Most of my records passed through Fred's, even the exotic ones. "Never heard of this one!" he'd say.

I'd use that as a selling point.

“Come on Fred, who *are* you exactly, a follower or visionary? An ordinary bloke or a prophet?”

“Oh, alright then, £1.50.”

It took quite a number of visits, I could only carry so much and the more you took the less he’d give you, that was simple economics. I would tape the records first so it wasn’t as if I’d lost them forever. I had boxes full of tapes, if only I could have sold them too.

Finally I’d raised enough and paid off both my dad and the tax man. I was back on the dole again, broke and living with my parents. Not for long, the demon brew, I simply couldn’t stop getting slaughtered, if I wasn’t pissing the bed I’d be almost setting the house on fire. Never try to cook while drunk, alcohol and heat don’t mix, and never, ever, fall asleep beneath an overloaded grill pan. I got into some terrible states, I didn’t seem to have an off-switch, I would drink until unconscious and worry about it afterwards. The following day could be confusing, once, the telly was covered in beans and another time the sides of my mouth were full of tiny lacerations. Couldn’t remember what I’d done, I couldn’t even hazard a guess, the whole thing drove me up the wall until I found that pipe of Pringles.

The last straw was a Saturday night, I stumbled home at four in the morning, somehow I had lost my keys and stood at the back door banging and shouting. No reply so I slept in the coal house. I was awoken a few hours later. “LOOK WHAT YOU’VE DONE!” my mother yelled as she dragged me angrily into the garden. It was like a bomb site, all those flowers and shrubs yanked up by the roots, strewn across the manicured lawn in a desperate and random fashion. Fortunately some flats were free and I got one very shortly after, being homeless I vaulted the queue and a fortnight later I was in.

My parents helped me out with the furnishings, after all I was still their son, I got a little drunk sometimes but other than that I was pretty harmless. They provided carpets, a TV, a few essential kitchen appliances, one of my aunts came up with a couch, then all I had to do after that was transfer all my stuff from the bedroom, carting it down one bit at a time, the wardrobe, bed and stereo system, my records, tapes and a few magazines.

The home brew didn't last much longer, the flat was little more than a bedsit, pretty soon it smelled like a brewery and since I was stuck in there on my own there were always people at the door expecting complimentary booze. The flats were arranged in blocks of four, two up, two down with a communal passageway, noisy buzzers on each door so the outer doors were often unlocked. I lived on the upper floor with a lovely view of countless rooftops, maybe on a decent day you could see some pylons off in the distance. Well, it was only Trimley, pleasant enough around by the church, but otherwise a council estate, boring, monotonous, featureless. Across the landing was Dopey Jimmy, he was pretty scary to look at, menacing eyes, a squashed-up mouth and a voice like a psychotronic robot. He was weird, I didn't trust him, I'd been told he was a thief, unsubstantiated rumours but most of my sources had proved reliable and my instincts were compatible. Gonna have to watch him, I thought, I didn't have so much worth stealing, still, the stuff I had was mine and I didn't want anyone pilfering it. The upper flats had a hatch to the loft, tucked away in a storage closet. *Hmm*, I thought, *an access point*. I felt a little vulnerable. I clambered up with a battered old torch and I was aghast with what I saw, the whole thing seemed to be open plan, a thief could slither in through a hatch and sneak back down through any other! I reported this to the council but no-one seemed to give a damn so I bought myself a set of bolts and clamped mine down from underneath.

28

Then a period of reflection. I had time and space to think. I'd done a fanzine, a record label, what the hell was I gonna do next? My punk career was pretty much over, I was getting sick of it all, I'd thought that punk could change the world but now it all seemed like a pipe-dream. Some bands had embraced heavy metal, much of it excruciating, some of them had turned to religion, the antithesis of punk. Some were dedicated Rastas, hardly the most PC of religions, yet somehow the punks didn't care, I cringed at the hypocrisy. Another band had just turned goth, not so much a capital crime but having been a hardcore band this new direction seemed quite jarring. Then they played the River View, I'd hoped they'd play a few old songs but nothing, nada, I was dejected, dreary was an understatement. Yes, change was necessary, sometimes it was even inspiring, off we went to Liverpool to check out Liam O' Kay's new band. They were great, much slower and rhythmic, but retaining a hardcore sound, intense and passionate, quite emotional, sadly, such a band was a rarity. Then there were the right-wing clowns, they were springing up all over, most had hung around since Oi! but never had they been so nazi. What was motivating them seemed rooted deep in ignorance. "The music's great!" an old mate said. I baulked at his stupidity. Punk, I thought, had lost all meaning, once they'd claimed it was a movement, that was something I'd never bought, from the very start there wasn't much unity. Most of the early bands were different, different styles and attitudes, a hundred punks, if you'd asked them, couldn't agree on what it meant. At first, it was simple rebellion, down with the old, in with the new; no-one cared if you could play as long as you were young and angry. Make a stand, think for yourself, at least till you were signed to a major and then it was just rock 'n' roll, tamed and moulded by the system. Even when the bands played on, disappearing underground, it all split into little factions, anarcho-punk, street-punk, post-punk; we clamoured for a better world, we wanted it, demanded it, but try and sell a fanzine at gigs and mostly folks would give you the brush-off. How had I shifted all those units? 5,000 records, 6,000 zines, by trading, that had been the key, giving and taking for mutual benefit. I looked back with mixed feelings, I had met some wonderful people, principled and dedicated, yet I could hardly call them friends. We all created our own little worlds and often lost ourselves inside them, walls built from rules and values, once we'd claimed there *weren't* any rules! Bands were preaching to the converted. Really? What did all *that* mean? Converted how? Converted to what? We were slowly drowning in rhetoric. Veganism, animal rights, worthy causes, yes indeed, but I lost count of the meat-free types who couldn't resist a bacon sandwich. Divided by political correctness, some adhered while others refused, some pretended to adhere, afraid they might be ostracised. Then there was anarchy, that old chestnut, chaos and destruction to some, to others it was love and peace, no wonder punk was so divided. Songs were really getting to me, 'Communion' by Funeral Nation, such an incredibly passionate song but deeply swathed in loss and sadness. Yes, there were a thousand zines and lots of independent labels, sharing ideas and information, yet I still felt isolated.

Often I'd just wander the streets, hoping for some inspiration. Though I had my independence I was now completely lost.

Jenson collared me one evening. "Wanna try some wobbly eggs?"

Wobbly eggs? What were *they*?

He dug a handful out of his pocket.

They were small and green and oval.

"What they like?"

"I dunno. Thought you'd like to try 'em first."

So I did. "I'll let ya know."

I'd done it at a party once, I'd found some tablets in a cupboard. "Neck them Eric!" So I did. Nothing too remarkable happened. I would either think too much or not at all which could cause problems. Never any middle ground. I simply hadn't found a balance.

Anyway, a mellow buzz. Delicate but rather soothing. That's what I reported back. Jenson wasn't too impressed.

Both of us preferred some drama.

"Got any mushies hidden away?"

He had, so I necked the lot, purchased with my final fiver.

What a blast it was that night, my very being seemed to dissolve, falling away, pixel by pixel, didn't know who the hell I was. I sat on the couch with a vacant stare, barely able to move my limbs, existing but in a state of bewilderment, floating, ethereal, detached. Still, inside I felt at peace, the spirit laid bare, devoid of emotion; for a moment or two at least, the universe began to make sense. I felt a connection with everything, even the bag of crisps beside me. "Look," I said, "you're sitting there and I don't even know what flavour you are!"

Later, when I went outside, I wandered through the empty streets. Everything seemed calm and still, the stars against a blackened sky. All that I could feel was space, up above and deep within. It wasn't too upsetting but it did reflect my isolation. I was so completely lost, exhausted and a little sad. It felt good to be alone but troubling to lack direction. Nothing was of interest, not books nor music, rarely humans. I was in an abject state. What was to become of me?

I hung around the betting shop, I didn't have much cash to spare but there was nothing else to do. Afternoon TV? Forget it. There were funny guys in there but most were either mad or drunk. No-one ever seemed to win. I found the whole thing quite depressing.

It was raining hard one night, so very hard I couldn't sleep. Raindrops pounded on the sill, repeatedly, relentlessly. I went downstairs and stood at the door with streams of water flooding by, reflections from the street lights warped by all that punishment from above. Then I heard some gentle footsteps, it was Bruce, a neighbour's dog. What was he doing out in this? The poor old thing looked soaked to the bone. Only one thing I could do, I stepped aside to let him in. He just stood and stared at me, then turned around and walked away.

Other titles by G.P. Rice:

DELIVERY - a novel

The first book of the Trimley Trilogy

Continues right where *Schemes* left off, the flat, desolate, full of frustration. Then, at once, a second chance. Will Eric make the most of it?

Paperback from Peagerm Press

Kindle version cheap on Amazon

Want one free? Look no further.

Yes, competition time!

In SCHEMES, many bands are alluded to, most with pseudonyms, others implied. Name them, or as many as you can, and if impressed, we'll send you DELIVERY.